ANTONIO VIVALDI

ARIE
PER SOPRANO
DA OPERE

RICORDI

(AZIO CORGHI)

La presente raccolta è frutto di una scelta operata nei manoscritti conservati presso la Biblioteca Nazionale di Torino. Scelta eterogenea che alla melodia semplice, cantabile, quasi popolareggiante contrappone una linea vocale più complessa non priva di influenze strumentali; all'aria di carattere fortemente drammatico accosta quella brillante, estrosa e fantasiosa, piena di virtuosismi canori. E questo nel tentativo di cogliere i molteplici aspetti del Vivaldi operista: ad una analisi attenta appare evidente la perfetta conoscenza della scrittura vocale e degli « effetti » che si possono richiedere alla voce in senso drammatico. Lo stanno a dimostrare le frequenti ripetizioni di proposizioni musicali intese a sottolineare con maggiore efficacia il testo; l'arditezza di certi intervalli melodici in parte giustificata dalla necessità espressiva e le insolite successioni di accordi dovute al procedere contrappuntistico delle parti; il gusto del cromatismo « ... per esprimere di più e meglio » contrastante il ritorno di lontani echi modali; l'impiego di scale minori di forma diversa sovrapposte che determinano curiosi incontri dissonanti e infine il particolare uso delle colorite « seste napoletane ».

Tuttavia questi procedimenti compositivi non vengono adottati unicamente seguendo l'estetica del tempo per cui, secondo il Du Bos, si possono imitare « il tono, gli accenti, i sospiri, le inflessioni della voce e infine tutti quei suoni di cui si vale la natura per esprimere i suoi sentimenti e le sue passioni », ma pure consentono a Vivaldi di difendere ed esaltare l'autonomia dei valori musicali. Si può dire pertanto che, attualmente, col graduale procedere verso una maggior conoscenza della produzione vocale vivaldiana, diventa sempre più possibile e doveroso non limitare l'abilità e la sapienza del compositore al solo campo della musica strumentale.

Per quanto riguarda la riduzione per pianoforte della partitura d'orchestra, si è cercato in linea di massima di riportare integralmente le linee strumentali; le poche aggiunte sono quelle suggerite dai numeri del basso continuo. I segni e le alterazioni posti tra parentesi non sono originali ma puramente indicativi e lasciano adito a soluzioni diverse. In alcuni casi sono state segnate alterazioni di precauzione onde evitare errate interpretazioni dovute soprattutto al tradizionale « senso della tonalità ».

The present collection is the result of a selection from manuscripts which are to be found in the National Library of Turin. It is a heterogeneous selection which includes simple lyrical, almost popular melodies together with more complex vocal lines with instrumental influences, and which compares strongly dramatic Arie with those which are brilliant and rich in fanciful virtuosity. It is therefore a collection intended to show the various aspects of Vivaldi as operatic composer. A careful analysis will draw attention to the composer's perfect familiarity with the voice and with the dramatic effects it can produce. This is further demonstrated by the frequent repetitions of some musical formulae which are particularly apt to underline the eloquence of the text. These are the bold melodic intervals, partly justified by dramatic needs, and the unusual successions of chords which arise from the contrapuntal pattern of the parts, also the use of chromatism, « ... to express more and better », contrasting the return to distant modal echoes, together with the employ of minor scales in different forms and superimposed in order to create curious dissonances, and finally the particular use of the colourful « Neapolitan sixths ».

These composition devices, however, are not adopted only to follow the aesthetic conventions of the time, thanks to which it should be possible, according to Du Bos, to imitate « the tone, accents, sighs, inflexions of the voice and also all those sounds which nature uses for the purpose of expressing feelings and passions », but also because they give Vivaldi the possibility to defend and exalt the autonomy of musical values. It may be said that a gradually increased knowledge of Vivaldi's vocal works brings with it a greater possibility to appreciate this composer's artistry even outside the field of instrumental music.

As far as the present edition is concerned, we have tried to adapt, as faithfully as possible, the piano version to the instrumental features of the score adding only those few notes which were suggested by the figured bass. The signs and alterations printed in brackets are not original but purely intended as indications and leave the interpreter free to come to different conclusions. In some cases, alterations have been marked merely as a precaution, to avoid erroneous interpretations which may be suggested by the traditional «sense of tonality ».

Die Herausgabe des hier vorgelegten Werkes ist das Ergebnis einer Auslese, die unter den in der Nationalbibliothek zu Turin aufbewahrten Manuskripten getroffen wurde. Das ausgewählte Werk ist insofern ungleichartig, als es der einfachen, sangbaren, fast dem Volkstümlichen zugewandten Melodik eine mehr komplizierte Führung der Gesangstimme gegenüberstellt, die nicht frei von instrumentalen Einflüssen ist. Zu der Grundhaltung von stark dramatischem Charakter tritt ein Element von Brillanz, Ausgefallenheit und Phantasiereichtum mit einer Fülle virtuoser Gesangseffekte. So ergibt sich bei dem Versuch, die vielschichtige Erscheinung des Opernkomponisten Vivaldi zu erfassen, folgendes: einer aufmerksamen Analyse offenbart sich deutlich die vollkommene Beherrschung der vokalen Schreibweise und der « Effekte », die von der Singstimme in dramatischer Hinsicht verlangt werden können. Das beweisen die zahlreichen Wiederholungen musikalischer Formulierungen, die darauf gerichtet sind, mit größtmöglicher Wirkung den Text zu unterstreichen, die Kühnheit gewisser melodischer Intervalle, die großenteils durch eine ausdrucksbedingte Notwendigkeit gerechtfertigt ist, dann die ungewöhnlichen Akkordfolgen, die durch das Fortschreiten der kontrapunktisch geführten Stimmen geboten sind, ferner das Vergnügen an der Klangfarbe, das dazu beiträgt, die Rückkehr von den damals üblichen entfernten Echos « mehr und besser » als Gegensatz zu gestalten, sodann die Verwendung übereinandergelegten Moll-Skalen verschiedener Gestalt, die zu eigenartigen dissonanten Zusammenklängen führt, und schließlich der bemerkenswerte Gebrauch des Kolorits « neapolitanische Sexte ».

Dennoch sind diese kompositorischen Verfahrensweisen nicht einzig und allein der Ästhetik der Zeit folgend angewandt, nach der, laut Du Bos, nachgeahmt werden können « der Ton, die Rufe, die Seufzer, der Tonfall von Stimmen und endlich alle jene Laute, deren die Natur sich bedient, um ihre Gefühle und ihre Leiden auszudrücken », aber sie erlauben durch Vivaldi, die Autonomie der musikalischen Werte zu verteidigen und hervorzuheben. Man kann deswegen sagen, daß gegenwärtig mit dem allmählichen Fortschreiten einer genaueren Kenntnis des vokalen Schaffens Vivaldis die Leistung und das Können dieses Meisters auch auf dem ihm eigenen Felde der Instrumentalmusik immer mehr und gebührend unbegrenzt an Auswirkungsmöglichkeit gewinnt.

Was den Klavierauszug dieser Partitur betrifft, so ist im Prinzip versucht worden, die instrumentalen Linien vollständig wiederzugeben. Die wenigen hinzugefügten Noten sind durch den bezifferten Basso continuo bedingt. Die in Klammern gesetzten Zeichen und Abwandlungen sind nicht original sondern nur Anregungen und lassen die Möglichkeit verschiedener Lösungen offen. Um interpretatorische Irrtümer zu vermeiden, sind in einigen Fällen aus Vorsicht Abänderungen eingezeichnet, die vor allem im Hinblick auf das traditionelle « Verständnis tonaler Musik » geboten erschienen.

INDICE

Antonio Vivaldi *(1678-1741)*

ARIE PER SOPRANO DA OPERE

Scelta, trascrizione e realizzazione del basso a cura di AZIO CORGHI

Guarda in quest'occhi e senti da *OTTONE IN VILLA*

Libretto di D. Lalli

1ª Rappresentazione: *Vicenza, 17 marzo 1713*

(F. 37 c. 104 r.)

Nelle pubbliche esecuzioni è obbligatorio inserire nei programmi il nome del revisore

CANTO

Guar da in que st'oc chi e sen ti, sen ti, sen ti

ciò che ti di ce il la bro, sen ti, sen ti ciò che ti

par la a mor, guar da in que st'oc chi e sen ti ciò che ti

par la a mor, guar da, guar da in que st'oc chi, sen ti

ciò che ti di_ce il la_bro, sen_ti, sen_ti ciò che ti_ par_la a_

_mor, sen_ti, sen_ti ciò che_ ti_ par_la a_mor.

(FINE)

4

Sol guar_da i__ miei tor _ men _ ti, e poi con un so_ _spir, con _ so _ la_il mio do _ lor, e poi__ con__ un__ so _ spir con _ so _ la_il mi _ o do _ lor,_____ il mio do _ lor.

D.C. al FINE

Col piacer della mia fede *da ARSILDA REGINA DI PONTO*

Libretto di D. Lalli

1ª Rappresentazione: *Venezia, primavera del 1716*

(F. 35 c. 20 v.)

6

fe - - o d'il _ lu_stre onor,

(mf)

bel tro _ fe _ o d'il _ lu_stre o_nor,

col pia_cer del_la_mia_ fe_de, al_ze_rò al tuo re_gio

pie _ de, bel____ tro_fe _ _ _

drà_____ di nuo _ vo al _

_ lor, lo splen _ dor di si bel gior _ no,

vin _ ci _ tor il crine a _ dor _ no ti _ ve _ drà_____

di nuovo allor.

D.C. al FINE

Io son quel gelsomino da *ARSILDA REGINA DI PONTO*

(F. 35 c.27 v.)

so-let-to se ne sta.

(mf)

Io son quel gel-so-mi-no vi-ci-no al ru-scel-

-let-to che asco-so tra l'er-bet-te, che asco-so tra l'er-bet-te so-let-to, so-

-let-to se ne sta, so-let-to se ne sta,

gel _ so _ mi _ no tra l'er _ bet _ te al ru scellet _ to, so _ let _ to, so _ let _ to, a _

_ sco _ so, gel _ so _ mi _ no se _ ne sta.

(FINE)

Ha sol con fresche erbet _ te di _

_letto a fa_vellar,   senza provar timor,   senza provar timor   che

sopra il suo candor,_____ a_pe a volar ne va.   Ha sol con fresche er_

_bet_te   dilet_to a fa _ vel _ lar,   senza provar ti_mor   che so_pra il suo can_

_dor,   a _ _ _ _ pe a vo lar____ ne va.

D.C. al FINE

Ben conosco a poco a poco da *ARSILDA REGINA DI PONTO*

(F. 35 c. 87 r.)

dal _ li pal _ pi _ ti del cor, ri _ ve _ gliar _ si il pri _ mo fo _ co

dal _ li pal _ pi _ ti del cor.

Ben co _ no _ sco a po _ co a

po _ co, ri _ sve _ gliar _ si il pri _ mo fo _ co, ri _ sve _ gliar _ si il pri _ mo

foco, a poco a poco, a poco a poco,

dalli palpiti del cor, _____ ri_sve

(mf)

_gliar_si il pri_mo fo_co dalli pal_pi_ti del cor, ri_sve

_gliar_si a poco a po___co, dalli pal_pi_

*) ms. originale:

D.C. al FINE

La pena amara da *LA VERITÀ IN CIMENTO*

Libretto di G. Palazzi e D. Lalli

1ª Rappresentazione: *Venezia, autunno del 1720*

(F. 33 c. 168 r.)

La pe _ na a ma _ _ _ ra che

senti in pet _ to,   spe _ ran _ _ _ _ _ za

ca _ ra ri_sa _ ne _ rà, _____

_ ri _ sa _ ne _ rà.

La pe _ na ama _ _ _ _ ra che

senti in pet _ to, spe _ ran _ za ca _ ra, spe _ ran _ za ca _ ra ri _

Cre - di al la spe - me non al__ so - spet - to, co -

- sì il tuo co - re go - der__ po - trà, go - der__ po - trà,__ go -

- der__ po - trà,__ go - der,__ go - der po - trà, go - der__ po -

- trà,__ go - der__ po - trà,__ go - der,__ go - der po - trà.

D.C. al FINE

Vedrò con mio diletto da *IL GIUSTINO*

Libretto di N. Berengani

1ª Rappresentazione: *Roma, carnevale del 1724*

(F. 34 c. 43 v.)

★) Accordi ben tenuti, un poco in rilievo la parte superiore.

181669

E se dal caro og-get-to lun-gi convien che si-a, convien che si-a, so-spi-re-rò pe-nan-do o-gni mo-men-to.

D.C. al FINE

Senza l'amato ben da *IL GIUSTINO*

(F. 34 c. 150 r.)

vi _ ve _ re que _ _ sto cuor non può, non sa.

Sen _ za l'a _ ma _ _ to ben,

vi _ ve _ re que _ sto sen _ non può, vi _ ve _ re que _ sto sen _ non

sa, non può, non sa, no, no, _ non può, non sa.

(FINE)

O, lie _ to ei vi _ vi an _ cor, o, se _ co que _ sto

cor mo _ rir,__ mo _ rir sa _ prà, o, se _ co

que _ sto cor mo _ rir,__ mo _ rir__ sa _ prà.

D.C. al FINE

Squarciami pure il seno da *IL TIGRANE*

Libretto di F. Silvani

1ª Rappresentazione: *Roma, carnevale 1724*

(G.37 c.12 r.)

*) Le prime cinque battute (identiche a quelle del "Presto" finale) sono state inserite dal revisore come introduzione.

squarciami pur il se _ no, ec _ co te l'offro ignu _ do, sen _ za ri _ pa _

_ ro o scu _ do, squar _ ciami il se _ no, squar _ _ cia _ mi il cor,

sen _ za ri _ paro o scu _ do il se _ no i _ gnu _ do, ec _ co che t'of _ fro il cor.

D.C. al FINE

Se lascio d'adorare da *IL TIGRANE*

(G.37 c.20 v.)

Allegro non molto

(mf)

(p)

Se
la-scio d'a-do-ra-re,— d'a-do-ra-re il bel che— mi_pia-gò, la_sci,

p

la-sci d'andar al ma-re,— la-sci d'andar al ma-re,— il ru-scel-let-to. Se

(mf)

34

*) sic.

131669

D. C. al FINE
(con ritornello)

Da quel ferro che ha svenato da *IL FARNACE*

Libretto di A. M. Luchini

1ª Rappresentazione: *Venezia, carnevale 1726*

(G. 36 c. 43 v.)

Da quel fer _ ro che ha sve _ na _ to

il___ mio___ spo _ so___ sven _ _ _ tu _ ra _ to,

im _ pa _ rai la cru_del _ tà, _____

___ la_ cru_del _ tà, la cru_del _ tà.

-rai la crudel _tà, _____

_____ la cru _ del _

_tà. Da quel fer _ ro ch'ha sve _ na _ to il mio

spo _ so sven _ tu _ ra _ to, ca _ ro_ spo _ so,_

spo _ so a _ ma _ to, im _ pa _ rai la _ cru _ del _ tà, im _ pa _ rai la _ cru _ del _

_ tà.

Nel mi _ ra _ re un

fi _ glio e _ san _ gue e ba _ gna _ to del mio

D.C. al FINE

Quel tuo ciglio languidetto da *IL FARNACE*

(G. 37 c. 140 r.)

ha sa - pu - to in - ca - te - nar,   ha sa -
-pu - to in - ca - te - nar,   ha sa - pu - to
in - ca - te - nar.
Quel tu - o ci - glio

_mo - re, ha____ sa _ pu_to in _ ca _ te _ nar,

ha ____ sa _ pu_to in _ ca _ te _ nar.

E quel _____ pla _ ci _ do sor _ ri _ so, il___ mio

pet _ to tut _ to_ af _ fet _ to, sem _ pre__ più fa in _

_ na _ mo _ rar, il mi _ o pet _ to tut _ to_ af _

_ fet _ to, sem _ pre__ più fa in _ na _ mo _ rar.

D.C. al FINE

Vorresti, il so, amor tiranno da *L'ATENEIDE*

Libretto di A. Zeno

1ª Rappresentazione: *Firenze, dicembre 1728*

(G. 39 c. 72 v.)

Allegro non molto

Vor_re_sti, il so, vor_re_sti, a_mor___ ti_ran___ ___no, dop_po*) la li_ber_tà, la li_ber_tà___ tor_mi la

*) sic.

181669

glo - - - - - ria, tor _ mi la

glo - ria.

Vor _ re _ stï, il so, il so, vor _ re _ sti a _ mor ___ ti - ran -

- no, dop _ po la li _ ber _ tà, la li _ ber _ tà,

★) ms. originale archi: ★★) ms. originale archi:

Ma _ la _ cau _ ta ra _ gion ve _ de il tuo in _ gan _ _ _ _ _ _ no e ti fa di _ spe _ rar la tua vit _ to _ _ _ _ _ ria, la tua vit _ to _ ri _ a, e ti fa di _ spe _ rar la tua vit _ to _ ri _ a.

D.C. al FINE

dedicata al "Farinello"

Sposa son disprezzata da *BAJAZET*

Libretto di A. Piovene (?)

1ª Rappresentazione: *Verona, carnevale del 1735*

(G. 36 c. 227 r.)

181669

za - ta, fi - da son oltrag - gia - ta, cie -

- li che fe - ci mai? Cie - li che fe - ci mai? E

pur egl'è il mio cor, il mio spo - so, il mio amor, la mia spe - ran -

- za.

Spo _ sa   son disprez_

_za _ ta,   fi _ da,   son ol_trag_gia _ ta,   cie _

_ li che fe_ci mai?   Cie _   _ li che fe_ci mai?   E

pur egli è il mio cor,   il mio spo _ so,   il mio a_mor,   la mia spe_

★) ms. originale:

Agitata da due venti da *LA GRISELDA*

Libretto di A. Zeno

1ª Rappresentazione: *Venezia, maggio 1735*

(F.36 c.175 r.)

A - gi - ta - ta da du - e ven - ti, fre - me l'on - da in mar tur - ba - to

e'l noc - chie - ro spa - ven - ta - to, spa - ven - ta - to,

già s'a - spet - ta a nau - fra - gar,

a nau _ fra _ gar, a nau _ fra _ gar.

A _ gi _ ta _ ta da du _ e

Dal do _ ve _ re e da l'a _ mo _ re com _ bat _ tu _ to, que _ sto co _ re non re _ si _ ste e par che ce _ da e in _ co _ min _ ci a de _ spe _ rar_____ a de _ spe _ rar, a de _ spe _ rar.

D. C. al FINE

Semblance Hypothesis of Memory
3rd edition

iUniverse books may be ordered through booksellers or by contacting:

iUniverse
1663 Liberty Drive
Bloomington, IN 47403
www.iuniverse.com
1-800-Authors (1-800-288-4677)

Because of the dynamic nature of the Internet, any Web addresses or links contained in this book may have changed since publication and may no longer be valid. The views expressed in this work are solely those of the author and do not necessarily reflect the views of the publisher, and the publisher hereby disclaims any responsibility for them.

ISBN: 978-1-4502-5620-9 (sc)
ISBN: 978-1-4502-5621-6 (ebook)

Printed in the United States of America

iUniverse rev. date: 10/01/2010

Semblance Hypothesis of Memory

3rd Edition

Kunjumon I. Vadakkan
M.B., B.S; M.D (Biochemistry)
University of Calicut, India
M.Sc.; Ph.D (Neuroscience)
University of Toronto, Canada

iUniverse, Inc.
New York   Bloomington

Dedicated to all my teachers

Preface to the 3ʳᵈ edition

From the results of the studies evolving from various fields of brain sciences, it can be seen that mechanism of memory is very complex. Semblance hypothesis was the result of an attempt to understand the order behind this seemingly complex process. In this attempt, I have used some freedom to seek new basic principles in order to put the pieces of the puzzle together. Since aligning of a few pieces that fit together does not necessarily lead to solving a large complex puzzle partially or completely, it was necessary to find the solutions (or at least feasible explanations) to maximum possible problems. Due to their interdependent nature and the fact that explanations for individual items do not stand by themselves, it was not possible to publish a regular-length article that support the claims of the hypothesis.

The initial work was published as the first edition of this book in 2007 named "Semblance of activity at the shared postsynapses and extracellular matrices: A structure-function hypothesis of memory". It was reasonable to argue that if the hypothesized mechanism for memory storage is correct, then we should be able to explain almost all the brain functions using the proposed mechanism and be able to replicate the mechanism outside the nervous system. This led to further examination of the hypothesis.

The present edition is completely rewritten. Chapter II explains the background and derivation of the semblance hypothesis of memory. Chapters III and IV examine the hypothesis in different physiological and pathological conditions respectively. Chapters V and VI explain how the hypothesis can provide theoretical requirements for a memory system. The principles and corollaries of the hypothesis are listed in chapter VII. Experimental results from various laboratories are explained in terms of the present hypothesis in chapter VIII. Methods for computational modelling are described in chapter IX. Finally, in chapter X, the importance and feasibility of developing intelligent machines based on the hypothesis is discussed.

It is not possible to find a perfect solution for a complex problem in one step. Words from Francis Crick and Christopher Koch in this regard are encouraging. *"A good framework is one that sounds reasonably plausible relative to available scientific data and that turns out to be largely correct. It is unlikely to be correct in all the details. A framework often contains unstated (and often unrecognized) assumptions, but this is unavoidable"* (21). The framework of the present hypothesis was evolved from the findings of experimental results from different laboratories in various fields of brain sciences. The main supporting evidence for the hypothesis is its ability to explain almost all the physiological and pathological features of the brain function.

Technical difficulties involved in studying the nature of the functional LINKs between the postsynaptic membranes of two synapses, the requirement of simultaneous fine-tuning of a very large number of variables and the fact that memory is a virtual sensation of a sensory stimulus that is available only to the internal state of the nervous system, make it difficult to test the hypothesis in biological system. Therefore, at this stage, I strongly feel that it may be easier to test the theoretical aspects of the hypothesis using computational modeling and applying the principles of the hypothesis in physical systems.

The efforts in developing and examining this hypothesis were made possible through the training that I had received from a large number of excellent teachers in various fields of science. I thank them all. My training at the University of Toronto, especially participation in the Program in Neuroscience, was highly influential. I thank all my colleagues for many stimulating discussions about the hypothesis. I thank all students, at various stages of my career, who had asked for better explanations.

I am grateful to Dr. John Roder, Canada Research Chair in learning and memory, for inviting me to present the hypothesis in 2007. I was fortunate to have many stimulating discussions about its philosophical and psychological aspects with Dr. Bibb Latané and the multidisciplinary faculty members at the Center for Human Science in Chapel Hill, U.S.A.

I am thankful to the faculty members at the Biomedical Sciences division of the Memorial University of Newfoundland, Biochemistry department at Calicut Medical College, India, and the Society for Neuroscience who provided opportunities to present the hypothesis. My training as a Neurology resident at the University of Manitoba has tremendously helped me to examine corroborative evidence for the hypothesis in various clinical conditions.

Finally, I thank iUniverse publishers for their efforts in publishing the work efficiently.

I am grateful to my ex-wife for supporting me to pursue science. I have no words to thank my daughter Pearl.

I am optimistic that the readers will consider this work in examining the experimental findings that arise from various studies. The semblance hypothesis should be considered as a work in progress and should be treated as unproven until it is verified against further experimental evidence. Results from further examination of the hypothesis will be posted at www.semblancehypothesis.org

Kunjumon Vadakkan
June, 2010

Contents

Abbreviations

AMPA	Amino-3-hydroxy-5-methyl- 4-isoxazolepropionic acid
AMPARs	AMPA receptors
BOLD	Blood oxygenation level dependent
CaMK II	Calcium/calmodulin-dependent protein kinase II
CA1/CA3	Cornu Ammonis 1/3 sub region of the hippocampus
CREB	cAMP/Ca^{2+} responsive element binding protein
ECM	Extracellular matrix
EPSP	Excitatory postsynaptic potentials
fEPSP	Field excitatory postsynaptic potential
fMRI	Functional magnetic resonance imaging
F→F	Function-function
F→S→F	Function-structure-function
FDG-PET	Fludeoxyglucose – positron emission tomography
FTP	Fronto-temporal dementia
GABA	Gamma amino butyric acid
LA	Lateral amygdala
LINK	This is not an abbreviation. The alphabets were highlighted to denote its significance
LTP	Long term potentiation
mEPSP	Miniature excitatory postsynaptic potential
NMDA	N-methyl-D-aspartate, a subunit of glutamate receptor channel
NS	Network semblance
PET	Positron emission tomography
Postsynapse	Postsynaptic membrane (dendritic spine)
RC	Recurrent collaterals
SEM	Shared extracellular matrix
S→F	Structure-function
SS	Synaptic semblance

I Summary

A multi-variable, multi-step problem of formation, storage and retrieval of memory may be solved by re-defining memory, such that the new elements of the definition can explain all the physiological and pathological features associated with memory leaving only a single variable to be solved. Once successful, the only remaining variable in the problem can be solved by experiments. In order to accomplish this, it was required to develop synthetic premises using available knowledge that can explain most of the physiological functioning of the nervous system. Those synthetic premises that lead to conclusions, that were able to explain various physiological and pathological features of the brain were then used to build the elements required for the hypothesis. Ability to replicate the same mechanism in physical systems can be considered as a gold standard for the discovery of mechanism of memory.

Semblance hypothesis was put forward to explain a possible mechanism for associative memory. The derivation of the hypothesis was carried through a reductive approach as following. The minimum statement to say that one synapse is activated is that its postsynaptic membrane (postsynapse) is activated. During one learning event, a specific set of postsynaptic membranes at different orders of neurons from the learned item ("item" means anything that relates to the real world) are activated. At a later time, artificial activation of this specific set of postsynapses (imagined by introducing electrodes to the brain) is assumed to induce memory for the learned event. Deriving from this, memory depends on the subset of postsynapses that are activated during retrieval, out of the set of postsynapses where changes took place during learning. This entailed the proposal of semblance hypothesis of memory.

A unit of memory, in the presence of an internal or external cue stimulus, results from the ability to induce specific postsynaptic events at the synapses of neurons from the learned item without the requirement of action potentials reaching their presynaptic sides. This may be viewed as true immediately following learning and was used for the derivation of the hypothesis. Activation of the postsynaptic membranes of the synapses activated by/represent/belong to the learned item is likely to induce a synaptic hallucination of the arrival of activity at their corresponding presynaptic terminals. This was named as semblance. Thus, memory is viewed as a virtual sensation of a sensory stimulus.

For achieving the above definition of a unit of memory, co-activation of fibers from the learned item and the cue stimulus (between different sensory inputs) during learning need to induce specific changes that will later allow the cue stimulus all by itself evoke activation of the set of postsynapses that belong to/represent the learned item (Fig.3). The first requirement is that the stimuli from the cue and the learned item need to converge at some locations within the brain. Hippocampus and amygdala are regions that receive inputs from almost all the sensory systems. Functional magnetic resonance imaging (fMRI) studies shows that increased oxygen release occurs at specific locations within the brain peaking at nearly four to five seconds after neuronal activity. These regions of blood oxygenation level dependent (BOLD) signals vary as cue stimulus changes. What mechanism can substantiate memory storage and retrieval using the varying oxygen requirements at different locations?

Semblance hypothesis proposes the formation of transient functional LINKs between the postsynapses of the cue and the learned item during learning. There is post-learning oxygenation requirement indicated by BOLD signals most probably to replenish the oxygen consumed at these regions for mechanisms that operate during learning. Similarly during memory retrieval, as the cue stimulus pass through various orders of neurons it may induce re-activation of functional LINKs which is followed by BOLD signals at these locations. Based on recent studies, it can be viewed that molecular oxygen is directly used for the functional LINK formation/re-activation or oxygen is used in those chemical reactions like oxidative phosphorylation that release energy for energy requiring steps during the LINK formation. During memory retrieval, oxygenation-state dependent functional LINKs can promote EPSP-spread from the postsynapses activated by the cue stimulus to the postsynapses that are activated by/represent/belong to the learned item. Activation of the postsynapses of the learned item without the activation of their presynaptic terminals evokes cellular hallucination of an action potential-induced synaptic transmission from the presynaptic membranes belonging to the learned item (Fig.4). This is named as synaptic semblance.

During memory retrieval using a cue stimulus, if more than one postsynapse (dendritic spine) of a neuron get depolarized, it may enable spatial and/or temporal summation of excitatory postsynaptic potentials (EPSPs) eliciting an action potential. The activity from this neuron propagates in the downstream network. These neurons, in which action potential is triggered, are neurons that belong to the learned item and induce "net work semblance" creating a hallucination of the sensory input from the learned item (Fig.7). The net effect of synaptic and network semblances occurring during memory retrieval results in "functional semblance", a virtual sensation of a stimulus in its absence, which is considered as memory. In other words, integrating simultaneous semblances generated at the synapses at each order of neuron (by combination) and the semblances generated in a temporal pattern at the synapses of different orders of neurons (by permutation) by a cue stimulus synthesize a multi-dimensional virtual sensation of a sensory stimulus, which is memory (Fig.11). Note that time is a dimension (due to synaptic delay at different neuronal orders) that need to be used in the integration process. Changes that may occur in the system due to synapse formation, elimination and neurogenesis also need to be incorporated.

In wakeful state, background sensory inputs and oscillating neuronal activities activate the nervous system continuously. As long as the nervous system cannot shut down, some of the background sensory inputs will always be there. Neuronal oscillations may be generated by receiving contributions from the lateral spread of activity through the functional LINKs. In a network of neurons that receives a continuum of inputs, instantaneous activation of a specific subset of postsynapses (through the functional LINKs) at different orders of neurons will induce semblance of a sensory input that the specific subset of postsynapses represent leading to memory.

Continued learning results in continued addition of postsynapses to the already LINKed postsynapses through new functional LINKs. These groups of postsynapses interconnected through functional LINKs are named as islets of functionally LINKed postsynapses (Fig.5). Maintaining the islets of functionally LINKed postsynapses intact is crucial for maintaining the integrity of associatively learned items, since the specificity of the semblance resulting from a cue depends on the specificity of the previously formed functional LINKs. In other words, the different islets of functionally LINKed postsynapses need to functionally remain separate from each other.

Since neurobiological experiments including electrophysiological studies to demonstrate the presence of functional LINKs between individual postsynapses are difficult to carry out due to technical difficulties, computational studies can be used for test the feasibility of semblance hypothesis. Since, semblances are virtual sensations of a sensory stimulus and are internal properties of a nervous system, computational approaches are required to further explore and understand the nature of the semblances.

One general argument is that any new hypothesis of memory should be able to explain the relationship between long-term potentiation (LTP) and memory. This can be explained as follows (Fig.19). When animals undergo novel associative learning, functional LINKs between two or more islets of functional LINKs form a mega-islet. Activation of a postsynapse of this mega-islet of LINKed postsynapses can cause spread of EPSP between its postsynapses. Since a subset of postsynapses in the mega-islet is already LINKed to one of the dendritic spines (postsynaptic membranes) on the dendritic tree of one CA1 neuron, multiple EPSPs from this subset will reach the main dendrite of the CA1 neuron simultaneously resulting in summated EPSP at this dendritic location sufficient to produce a corresponding increase in current sink in the extracellular matrix. The extracellular signal recorded from the apical dendrites of a population of pyramidal neurons in the stratum radiatum of the CA1 region in response to Schaffer collateral stimulation, namely the field EPSP, will now show an increase in amplitude and contribute to an increase in fEPSP slope showing LTP.

Misconnection between the islets of functionally LINKed postsynapses reduces the formation of specific semblances by producing non-specific semblances through the misconnections with the unrelated islets of LINKed postsynapses. This can result in hallucinations seen in many disease conditions including psychiatric disorders.

Functionally, at least three types of semblances can be visualized - primary, secondary and tertiary. Neuronal activity during hippocampal and cortical oscillations as well as those that are triggered by background environmental stimuli activates a set of neurons that result in the formation of highly non-selective semblances named as primary semblances. They are characteristic of the species and include consciousness. Secondary semblances include those that occur in the presence of specific cue stimulus. Examples include memory, path finding, and qualia of color, sound, smell, touch, taste and pain. Tertiary semblance occurs in response to a novel cue stimulus that was not used in any associative learning before.

Behavioural activity is often guided by the semblances and the accompanying partial neural network activities that guide the execution of appropriate motor actions. Activities of the partial neural network, that are activated through structural LINKs, can explain the innate behaviours of the newborns like rooting and sucking reflexes that occur in the absence of any prior learning. Acute survival responses may depend on the motor responses guided by the activation of the partial network belonging to the learned item.

How can a nervous system respond to a novel cue particularly if it evokes more than one semblance of nearly equal strengths? When responses to a novel cue results in more than one semblance that leaves the animal to choose from, probability remains as the only guiding principle. This makes it similar to the probability calculations used in quantum indeterminacy (Fig.15).

Importance of the formation of a unique semblance for every possible cue stimulus from the environment as a guiding principle for evolutionary adaptation is discussed. Requirement for sophisticated tools to examine the transient functional LINKs through possible ultra-structural studies are also discussed. The functioning of the oxygenation state dependent functional LINKs required for the hypothesis and its testability in physical systems is explained. Finally, development of intelligent machines is discussed.

Semblances, even though may seem to have no physical attributes, are regarded as a fundamental principle of the operation of the nervous system since we can explain almost all the physiological and pathological functioning of the nervous system through this property. It provides explanation for many unexplained brain functions. Examples include mechanism of memory retrieval at physiological time-scales, functional role of neurogenesis, consolidation, relationship between memory and LTP, and a feasible explanation for hallucinations. In summary, semblance hypothesis provides means to explain many unexplained brain functions and bridge unconnected findings in various fields of brain sciences.

II Semblance hypothesis of memory

II.1 Introduction

Hebb's postulates (51) have been extended to examine activity-dependent strengthening and weakening of synaptic connections through synaptic plasticity changes. Long-term potentiation (LTP) of N-methyl-D-aspartate (NMDA) channels is one of the synaptic plasticity changes that have been shown to correlate with learning (8, 84, 86, 94, 146, 162). In theoretical neuroscience, activity-dependent synaptic changes are measured as synaptic weights and encoding of their patterns are considered as the primary basis of learning. Specifically, stable high-resolution synaptic weight values are considered as feasible physical substrates for long-term memory (2, 73, 79). Correlation between synaptic weight changes and plasticity changes during learning were examined by different modeling studies (116, 154). However, the link between abstract synaptic weights and the physical substrate for long-term memory was shown to be weakened by experimental results (116). A separate mechanism for memory storage by non-glutamatergic synapses involved in learning (161) is not yet known.

Computational studies using available data have shown the possibility for memory loss due to overwriting of the established pattern of synaptic connectivity as one of the limiting factors of the current hypotheses and have led to the suggestion for a more radical modification of the standard model of memory storage for improving memory performance (39). Absence of plasticity changes during memory retrieval, growth of new synaptic connections, synapse elimination and neurogenesis are additional constraints in the search for basic elements of the neural code associated with specific memory representation (12).

Modifications of the synaptic plasticity hypothesis were also examined as potential candidates. They include the synaptic tagging hypothesis and the calcium/calmodulin-dependent protein kinase II (CaMK II) hypothesis (37, 74). In addition, cortical rewiring, propagation through prion proteins, and the involvement of quantum mechanics were also considered as potential candidates (15, 105, 115). Post-translational modification of existing proteins was also proposed as a possible mechanism for long-lasting memory (124). However, it is not yet known how plasticity changes during learning are used to store memories that can later be retrieved at physiological time-scales without the requirement of similar or reversed form of plasticity changes.

Major approaches towards discovering the mechanism of memory was based on genetic and biochemical defects found in various disorders that showed symptoms of memory loss. These include a) mutations in the genes of amyloid precursor protein (APP), presenilin-1 protein (PS-1) and presenilin-2 protein (PS-2) in Alzheimer's disease b) mutations in gene of microtubule associated protein tau (MAPT) in fronto-temporal dementia (FTD) c) formation of inclusion bodies positive for ubiquitin, a 76 amino acid protein, forming part of a cytoplasmic system for degradation and digestion of other intracellular proteins in the granule neurons of the dentate gyrus in FTD d) formation of Lewy bodies, intracytoplasmic eosinophilic neuronal inclusions containing the protein alpha-synuclein aggregated with abnormally phophorylated neurofilaments and ubiquitin in dementia with Lewy bodies, and e) accumulation of an abnormal partially protease-resistant isoform known as prion protein in prion disease.

The above disorders involve defects in different unrelated proteins in different areas of the brain resulting in memory defects. How can a feasible mechanism of memory be derived using loss of function of these proteins in above disease conditions? There are two main possibilities. 1) The above proteins are likely to be part of a chain of molecular events associated with memory storage. 2) There is an epi-mechanism for memory storage encompassing all these molecules. There is no evidence for the first possibility since a) no known biochemical pathways that incorporates all these molecules are known b) even if an unknown pathway exist, retrieval of memories using a biochemical pathway is unlikely to meet the required time-scales of memory retrieval. Therefore, we will consider the second possibility of an epi-mechanism for further examination.

Another important area that needs to be introduced is the fact that memory storage mechanism is widely distributed in the nervous system. Lesions of any one of the structures of the Papez's circuit (cingulate gyrus – entorhinal cortex – hippocampus – fornix – mamillo-thalamic tract – anterior nucleus of thalamus – cingulate cortex) has shown memory defects. Lesions of isolated regions of the cortex have also shown memory defects. For example, right hemisphere stroke involving the parietal lobe in humans produce moderate impairment of memory (72). These indicate that the memory is stored widely in the brain even though lesions of some regions of the brain have increased susceptibility to cause memory loss. These areas of increased susceptibility could be regions of increased neuronal/synaptic densities or regions through which large number of fibers that are involved in memory pass through. In short, no single area of the brain exclusively encodes all the memories; instead encoding of memories takes place widely across the brain.

Based on the duration of storage, memory is classified into working, short term and long term memories. However, based on the similarity in the time-scales of retrieval of these different memory types, it may be argued that their retrieval mechanisms are same. It is possible that a similar mechanism of encoding with varying duration of storage by different factors is a feasible mechanism and is examined in the present work.

An episodic representation of an event is organized as an order of events that unfolds as a mental replay of the event spread over time (148). Memory for each event can be de-constructed into a series of associative representations of the learned items ("item" means anything that relates to the real world). Thus it is possible to deconstruct and the reconstruct the basic mechanisms involved in the memory storage and retrieval process.

In general, unless we recall memory in the presence of a specific cue (internal or external), its retrieval does not take place. During memory retrieval, sensory inputs from the learned item are not present to activate the initial sensory neurons. It may then be assumed that memory is a virtual sensation which is a function of specific changes occurred during learning.

It is difficult to carry out reductionistic studies to find physical mechanisms directly linking to a virtual sensation. This substantially reduced our ability to study how memories are retrieved from yet another unknown state of memory storage. We were limited to identifying and studying the changes occurring during learning that can induce long-term changes. Long duration of ion channel open-state and biochemical cascades that are associated with learning were used in hypotheses to test their association with long-term memory. It was difficult to establish either causality or retrieval-efficiency based on the similarities in the long duration of these events. Even though protein synthesis, trafficking and modifications follow learning, their time-scales are not correlated with those of the acquisition or retrieval of different types of memories.

The present consensus is that memories are distributed across a population of neurons. Both experimental (43, 49, 149) and computational (70) studies have shown activation of specific neurons by specific cues during memory retrieval. It is not known how activities of these neurons contribute towards memory retrieval. The present work examines a feasible mechanism that supports memory retrieval at appropriate time-scales leading to the virtual sensation of sensory inputs. Abstracts of the earlier editions of the work were presented at the Canadian Association for Neuroscience (151) and Society for Neuroscience annual meetings (152, 153).

II.2 Need for new hypotheses for memory

A gold standard for the discovery of memory storage mechanism will be to the ability to replicate the mechanism in physical systems. Since large number of complex issues needs to be solved, making a hypothesis and testing it theoretically before carrying out experimental verifications is a reasonable step. Hypothesis development is very important since the computations of the features (we don't know yet what features are to be computed) from nearly 10^{10} neurons and 10^{15} synapses are required to understand the mechanism. A single counter example/proof against a hypothesis can then be used as a sufficient reason to modify/reject it. One characteristic feature of a hypothesis is that it must be falsifiable. i. e. it must at least in principle be possible to make an observation that would disprove the proposition as false, even if one has not actually (yet) made that observation (117). Once such an observation is made, it will lead to the rejection of the hypothesis. However, with the rejection of a hypothesis, we are likely to make some conclusions that will aid in the development of newer and better hypotheses.

One of the ways to examine any hypothesis of memory is to test its ability to explain all the physiological and pathological features associated with memory given in Table 1. Hypotheses that can provide a broader framework incorporating the following features need to be built and tested theoretically followed by experimental approaches to confirm their validity.

Table 1. List of required features of memory that are needed to be supported by a hypothesis

1. Retrieval of memory at physiological time-scales

2. Provision for unlimited memory life-times (125)

3. Absence of overwriting of old memories by new ones (125)

4. Absence of decay of the memory trace by any modification of the basic units by new learning (125)

5. Instant access to very large memory stores (1)

6. Ability of the mechanism/system to generate hypothesis (1)

7. Provisions for interaction between internally generated hypotheses and external evidence that allows sensory data to veto or support internal constructs extremely efficiently (1)

8. Ease of learning a related task

9. Disuse reduction in memory

10. Mechanism for retaining specificity of memory retrieval

11. Functional integration and operation of hippocampal new neurons in learning and memory

12. Explanation for consolidation of memory – How memories are transferred from the hippocampus to the cortex?

13. Transfer of the basic units of memory for a different learning and retrieval event (22)

14. Ability to explain the correlation between LTP and memory

15. Ability to explain mirror neuron activity

16. Ability to examine/explain features of psychiatric disorders, if possible

17. Ability to replicate the hypothesized mechanism in physical systems, if possible

18. Ability to find a reasonable relationship between memory and consciousness since some form of memory is associated with consciousness

19. A cellular mechanism that can support the lack of cognitive access to the internal states and representations of perceptual systems.

In summary, an ideal hypothesis should be able to substantiate the molecular, cellular, electrophysiological, systems and behavioural features of all the brain functions.

II.3 Derivation of the hypothesis using synthetic premises

Hebb's predictions (51) have been rigorously tested by experiments. Reductionistic approaches were used extensively in understanding the biochemical changes supporting plasticity changes. These approaches were able to identify key molecules associated with learning through "loss of function" studies by genetic and pharmacological interventions. In complex situations, hypothesis-driven experiments are usually carried out with falsifiability of the hypothesis (117) as an easy way for eliminating a hypothesis at an early stage. According to an alternate view, a hypothesis may not lead to good scientific inquiry since it provides the initiative and incentive for the inquiry and governs its actual form (89). Therefore, a highly objective approach for its discovery to accomplish all the requirements listed in Table 1 need to be undertaken. With this aim, theoretical examination of the neurobiological problem of memory was carried out to derive the present hypothesis.

Generally, hypotheses in biology are derived from straightforward logical steps or situations involving few steps of unsolved issues sandwiched between known facts. However, issues of storage and retrieval of memories are too complex to find a solution through a direct hypothesis-driven approach. This inherent difficulty may be solved by designing novel philosophical approaches as follows. The premises of an argument are a set of propositions (that are *assumed to be true)* from which the conclusion of the argument is drawn. Using inductive reasoning approaches, synthetic premises (36) (that are either true or false) that can offer some degree of support (but less than complete support) of the claim being made can be derived (Fig.1).

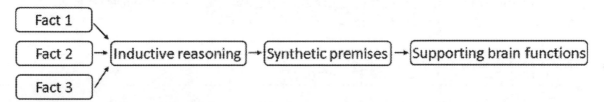

Figure 1. A schematic representation showing the method of derivation and application of synthetic premises used for the present work. Those synthetic premises that can explain most of the brain functions can be used to test whether the anticipated cellular and molecular changes exists using experiments.

Synthetic premises from basic synaptic structures using inductive reasoning approach were developed and were theoretically examined to test whether they lead to conclusions that fit with various physiological and pathological conditions. This process of building and applying different premises were continued until successful ones were found. It was necessary to view memory as a virtual sensation of a sensory stimulus to develop synthetic premises that lead to the derivation of the hypothesis. After deriving such synthetic premises, and examining that those premises provide support for the conclusions by examining the form of the argument, the synthetic premises can be tested to see whether they are true or false in actuality through experimental approaches. Synthetic premises offer flexibility in testing theoretically whether the newly derived basic units can lead to a mechanism of memory storage.

II.4 Semblance hypothesis

The semblance hypothesis was developed from the basic question how memory can be retrieved at physiological time-scales when a cue stimulus makes a search. The semblance hypothesis was derived to explain associative learning and memory retrieval through a series of inductive reasoning steps using some key assumptions. The main purpose was to build a broader frame work that can incorporate all the elements that were mentioned in section II.2. Once this is achieved, fine-tuning of the features can be carried out to approach towards the cellular and molecular mechanisms.

During a given learning event, the postsynaptic membranes of a specific set of synapses along different orders of neurons from the learned item are activated. Following this, artificial activation of this specific set of postsynaptic membranes (imagined by introducing electrodes into the brain) is assumed to induce memory for the learned event, similar to the assumptions used to explain short term synaptic facilitation as a mechanism of working memory (92). How can a similar type of a mechanism work for long-term storage? Can activation of a different set of synapses provide an equivalent mechanism enabling retrieval of the same memories? Answers to these questions are addressed in the present work.

The derivation of the hypothesis has two major stages. Each stage consists of a series of steps that are numbered.

Stage I

1. For the purpose of derivation of the hypothesis, memory is viewed as a virtual sensation of a sensory stimulus since the sensory inputs from the item that is memorized is not present during the retrieval of memory.

2. We store thousands of memories. A specific internal or external cue stimulus is required to retrieve a specific memory.

3. In the classical Pavlovian experiments, the conditioned and unconditioned stimuli were very distinct items reaching different sensory systems. Stimuli reaching different sensory systems are not mandatory for associative learning and its retrieval. Elements within a single learned item (say for example, one feature of a bell) can be used as a cue for retrieving memories of the learned item (the bell).

4. Let us now conduct an imaginary experiment by looking at a violet-coloured pen. During this, let us assume that a specific set of 10^5 synapses (out of the total 10^{15} synapses in our brain) were activated at different orders of neurons (1st order being the neurons in the optic nerve). After one day, let us insert 10^5 electrodes into the brain to stimulate those specific 10^5 synapses. Stimulate them in the same temporal order as would have happened when we visualised the pen during learning. Note that those synapses in the same order of neurons are likely to get activated simultaneously. Those at different orders of neurons get activated in a temporal sequence. The temporal order

of activation is important for computational work at later stages of the hypothesis.

5. During this stimulation, it is assumed that we are likely to memorize/ imagine/visualize that violet-coloured pen. This leads to the possibility that by activating the specific set of 10^5 synapses out of the total 10^{15} synapses memory can be achieved (by using permutation, (the events activated with a specific order from lower to higher orders of neurons). The chances of this taking place is = one in $10^{15}!/(10^{15}-10^5)!$ = one in $10^{15}!/(10^{10}!)$ = one in 10^{65}. This demonstrates the specificity of the mechanism by which memory can be retrieved)).

6. During normal memory retrieval, how can we activate a specific set of 10^5 synapses out of the total 10^{15} synapses? If we know the mechanism to activate one of those 10^5 specific synapses, then we can extend the same mechanism to all the 10^5 synapses.

7. Now we can address the issue in a modified way. What is the minimum condition that suggests activation of a synapse? Activation of the postsynapse (postsynaptic membrane) can be taken as the equivalent of activating a synapse since the activation of a postsynapse requires the arrival of an action potential at its presynaptic terminal, neurotransmission and EPSP generation at the postsynapses.

8. Since there is no sensory stimulus available from the item to be memorized, we cannot anticipate any action potential reaching at the presynaptic terminals. Therefore, we need to activate the postsynapses of the synapses that represent the learned item without any action potential reaching their presynaptic terminals during memory retrieval. *Activation of a postsynapse without the arrival of an action potential at its presynaptic terminal (at the synaptic level) can very well represent the idea of evoking a virtual sensation of a sensory stimulus (at the systems/behavioural level).* In other words, the activation of a specific set of postsynapses that can evoke virtual sensation of a sensory stimulus is expected during retrieval of memory.

9. At this point we come across with two key questions. 1) Can we activate the postsynapse of a synapse in the absence of the arrival of an action potential at the presynaptic terminal? 2) How can we choose those 10^5 specific postsynapses from the total 10^{15} synapses for specific activation? What we have is a specific cue stimulus that activates a set of cue-specific synapses. We can now arrive at a simple question at the synaptic level: "How can we activate a specific set of 10^5 postsynapses that represents the item to be retrieved in the presence of the activation of a specific set of synapses by the cue stimulus?

10. Let us assume that the cue stimulus evokes the activation (we mean EPSP for convenience; other changes are also considered and discussed in section

II.6) of the postsynaptic membranes of the synapses that identify/represent the learned item. Then it is reasonable to argue that some of the synapses through which activity spreads from the cue stimulus should be physically close enough to some of the postsynapses that identify the item to be memorized. In addition, a mechanism should exist that can cause the spread of activity from the synapses of the cue stimulus to the postsynapses of the item to be memorized (Fig. 2).

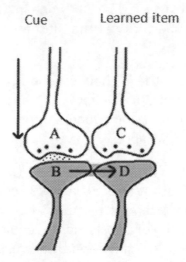

Cue   Learned item

*Figure 2. Illustration of the hypothesized EPSP-spread during memory retrieval. The cue stimulus reaching presynaptic terminal **A** depolarizes its postsynaptic membrane **B**, and the EPSP spreads to postsynaptic membrane **D**. This can only happen provided there is a functional LINK (see explanation of functional LINK in step 11) between the postsynapses **B** and **D**. Therefore, we can assume that a functional LINK is required to be formed between the postsynapses **B** and **D** during learning.*

11. Since physical closeness between the postsynapses **B** and **D** (in figure 2) is required for learning associated changes to take place, it can be assumed that for associative learning to occur the sensory inputs from the cue and the item to be retrieved should inevitably converge at some brain locations. It is known that sensory inputs from different sensory endings reach their representative cortices and then after a few more neuronal orders reach the entorhinal cortex, hippocampus and locations within the Papez's circuit. At these locations of convergence of sensory inputs, synapses from the cue stimulus find physical closeness to the postsynapses of the item to be memorized.

12. What should be the critical change occurring during learning between the synapses that are activated by the cue and the postsynapses that represent/ identify the item to be learned that can later represent the learned item during memory retrieval? We can at least assume that during learning a functional LINK (the word functional was used to indicate that it is a function of the activity in either one of the postsynapses; the word LINK is written in capital letters to indicate that it is the key element of the hypothesis and

that we have to explore it further to discover its exact nature) is established between the postsynapses of the cue stimulus and the item to be learned (Fig.3). Functional LINKs can be viewed as transient (as a function of the specificity of the cue stimulus) to substantiate retrieval of large number of memories using a system with finite number of synapses. The functional LINKs as the building units have the advantage that as the cue features changes, the postsynapses activated through the functional LINKs changes and the retrieved memory is also changed (mechanism is explained in section II.4, stage II).

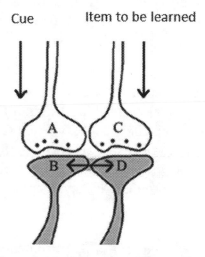

Cue   Item to be learned

*Figure 3. Illustration showing the hypothesized functional connection (LINK) formed between the two postsynaptic membranes **B** and **D** during learning. The functional LINK is transient and is a function of the specific nature of the cue stimulus which determines its activation. Re-activation of the functional LINK requires activation of either one of the postsynapses (**B** or **D**).*

13. During learning, co-activation of synapses from the learned item and the cue stimulus needs to induce specific changes that will later allow the cue stimulus by itself to evoke the activation of the set of postsynaptic membranes that belong to the learned item. This leads to the generation of the semblance hypothesis. *A unit of memory, in the presence of an internal or external cue stimulus, results from the ability to induce specific postsynaptic events at the synapses of the neurons from the learned item without the requirement of action potentials reaching their presynaptic sides.*

14. The proposed LINKs formed during learning can be of three different types and may operate as following.

A. Function-Function (F→F) LINKs: These are transient, activity and oxygenation-state-dependent functional LINKs formed during learning. During cue-induced synaptic activity, re-activation of the functional LINKs that were formed during learning takes place resulting in the spread of EPSP eliciting semblance (see step 14). The half-life of these (F→F) LINKs is discussed in section II.8.1.

B. Function-Structure-Function (F→S→F) LINKs: When the functional LINKs are repeatedly activated over a long period of time (by different learning events) they eventually get converted to LINKs where EPSP-spread may occur even at sub-threshold conditions. Details are given in section II.8.2.

C. Structural LINKs: These LINKs can be viewed as genetically determined. They can be responsible for survival behaviours in newborns in the absence of any prior learning (examples include grasp, rooting, and sucking reflexes that are essential for survival and operate in the absence of any prior learning experiences). Details are given in section II.8.3.

15. Let us examine the effects of EPSP-spread through the LINKs. When the cue stimulus arrives at the synapse **A-B** (in Fig.4), EPSPs generated at the postsynapse **B** of the synapse will spread through the functional LINKs to the postsynapse **D** that represent/identify the learned item. When the postsynapse **D** is depolarized in the absence of the arrival of an action potential at its presynaptic terminal **C**, then the postsynapse **D** gets a cellular hallucination of an action potential reaching its presynaptic side **C**, resulting in "synaptic semblance".

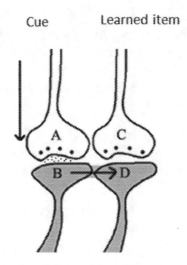

Cue   Learned item

*Figure 4. During retrieval, the cue stimulus reaching the presynaptic terminal **A** depolarizes its postsynaptic membrane **B**, and the EPSP spreads through the functional LINK to the postsynaptic membrane **D**. This evokes cellular hallucination, at the postsynapse **D**, of an action potential reaching its presynaptic terminal **C**. This was named "synaptic semblance".*

16. When the related learning events continue, one of the postsynapses (either **B** or **D** in the figure 5) will be involved in the formation of functional LINKs with the postsynapses of the neighbouring synapses (seen as additional postsynapses on the right side of the postsynapse **D** in the left panel, Fig.5).

As this process continues, it will result in the formation of islets of LINKed (LINKable/re-establishable during retrieval) postsynapses (see right panel, Fig.5 where islets of LINKed postsynapses are showed in a hypothetical cross-sectional view). Details of the expanding functional LINKs is given as a separate section (section II.9).

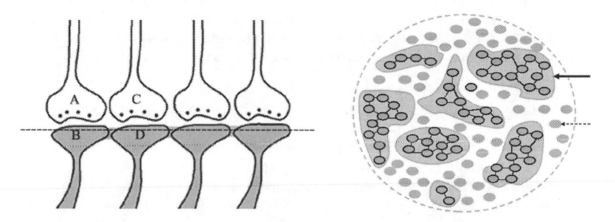

Figure 5. Left panel: Illustration showing LINKable postsynapses.

*Left panel: Multiple dendritic spine heads belonging to dendrites of different neurons can become functionally LINKed to each other upon coincident activation. Only two presynaptic terminals (**A** and **C**) and two postsynapses (**B** and **D**) are marked. Two more synapses are placed on the right side of the synapse **C-D**. The dotted line shows a cross-section across all the postsynapses. A cross-sectional view of the postsynapses is given in the right panel.*

Right panel: A hypothetical cross-sectional view through the postsynapses of nearly hundred synapses that are close to and parallel to each other in a brain region (see the horizontal dotted line across the postsynaptic membranes in the left panel). In this illustration, we imagine that the cut surfaces of the postsynaptic membranes are in the same plane and are shown in small dark circles (broken arrow). When learning occurs, functional LINKs between simultaneously activated postsynapses are formed (A LINK between two postsynapses is shown nearly after the 6'O clock position). Continued learning using any of those already connected synapses will increase the number LINKed postsynaptic membranes forming islets of functionally LINKed postsynapses (solid arrow). Multiple LINKs between the postsynapses in an islet can cause the spread of EPSP between the postsynapses within an islet. The individual islets are expected to be functionally separate from each other.

17. Functional LINK forms as a function of the arrival of activity in both postsynapses that get LINKed. Functional LINK is re-activated as a function of the arrival of activity in either one of the postsynapses that was previously LINKed.

18. Now let us examine whether the role of the proposed functional LINKs match with any known physiological changes. It can be done by asking the question, "Can EPSP-spread through the functional LINKs between the postsynapses during their establishment (during learning) or re-establishment (during retrieval) depends on any known factors essential during learning or memory

retrieval?" Let us first examine some of the key factors upon which learning and memory retrieval depend on. Increased use of oxygen and glucose at locations of brain involved in learning and memory retrieval were extensively studied using fMRI and brain 2-[^{18}F] fluoro-2-Deoxy-D-glucose-positron emission tomography (FDG-PET) studies. Examination of the relationship between the above factors and the proposed functional LINKs show that functional LINK formation is likely to depend on oxygenation state and glucose usage at specific locations in the brain. Future experiments (see section VIII) may provide us further information about the nature of the functional LINKs.

19. During retrieval of memory, two possible events can occur. 1) Activation of the postsynaptic membranes belonging to the learned item will lead to synaptic semblance. 2) EPSP-spread through LINKed postsynapses may reach sufficient number of postsynapses (dendritic spines) that belong to/represent the learned item and get summated to generate an action potential (as for the neurons **S** and **T**, Fig.7).

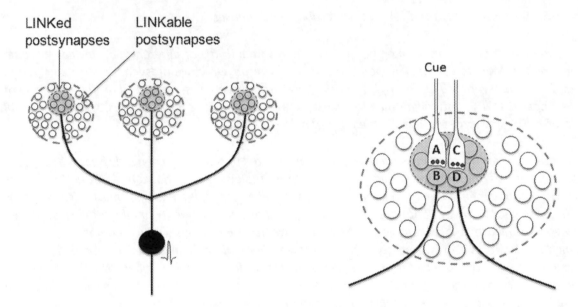

*Figure 6. Schematic representation showing how spatial summation of EPSPs from different postsynapses (dendritic spines) on the dendritic tree of a neuron takes place. Provided sufficient number of EPSPs reaches these postsynapses through the functional LINKs they can get spatially or temporally summated (along with EPSPs from normal synaptic transmission) to evoke an action potential at the axon hillock. Right panel shows that the cue stimulus depolarizes the postsynapse **B** that can propagate to the postsynapse **D** through the functional LINK.*

20. Activation of a neuron that represents/belongs to the learned item leads to the activation of a partial neuronal network (Fig.7). The activation of a partial network of neurons that belong to/represent the learned item without the need of any sensory stimuli from the learned item provide "network semblance". Network semblance means activation of a specific network

occurring at a specific neuronal order without activation of their synaptically connected (not through the LINKs) penultimate neuronal orders, providing cellular hallucination of sensory inputs reaching those penultimate orders of neurons from the learned item.

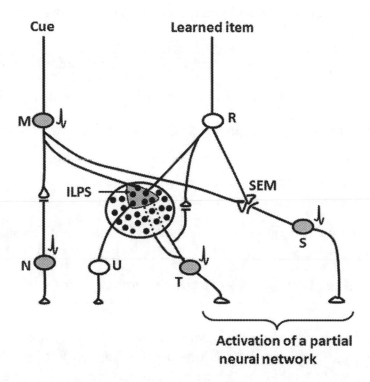

*Figure 7. Schematic representation of activation of a partial neuronal network occurring during the retrieval of an associative memory. A cue stimulus activates neuron **M**. The action potential reaches an islet of LINKed postsynapses (ILPS; shown as a shaded triangular area) and a shared extracellular matrix (SEM). In both these functional units, EPSPs can spread to the postsynaptic membranes of the neuronal terminals belonging to the learned item. Two consequences occur. First, a semblance of activity from the learned item occurs at the synapses of the axonal terminals of the neuron **R** belonging to the learned item. (Note that semblance at the ILPS occurs concurrently with the neuronal activity of **T**. Similarly, semblance at the SEM occurs concurrent with the neuronal activity of **S**). Second, the spread of EPSP can contribute to the generation of action potentials at the axon hillocks of the neurons **T** and **S** belonging to the learned item. Even though EPSP arrives at one of the postsynapses of the neuron **U** (at the ILPS) and induces synaptic semblance, it will not lead to generation of action potential in the neuron **U** due to lack of sufficient EPSPs to summate to reach the threshold for action potential generation.*

21. The optimal combination of synaptic and network semblances can provide net functional semblance for memory retrieval. Details are given in the stage II of the derivation of the hypothesis. Various factors that affect the strength of the net semblance for memory are listed in Table 2.

Table2. Factors that determine the net functional semblance though LINKed postsynapses from different orders of neurons.

1. Previous learning events that have already established functional LINKs between the postsynapses from the related cues and the related item to be learned

2. Total number of the LINKed postsynapses in all the orders of a neuron

3. Total number of orders of neurons where the cue stimulus reaches

4. Synaptic and network semblances occurring through the functional LINKs

5. Threshold number of LINKable postsynapses required for functional semblance leading to memory

6. Specificity and strength of the cue that evokes functional semblance for a specific memory

7. Size of LINKed postsynapses at a given neuronal order

22. Possible mechanism of long-term memory storage occurring through dynamic and expanding functional LINKs is explained in section II.9. In addition to providing network semblance, the partial neuronal network that belongs to/ represents the learned item may also be involved in behavioural changes associated with memory retrieval. This is discussed in sections VI.13).

Stage II

In the stage I, we have derived both synaptic and network semblances. What does semblance mean? How can these semblances be put together to evoke the virtual sensation of the sensory stimulus from the learned item? This is explained through the following steps.

1. Let us assume that the synaptic semblance occurs at one specific CA3-CA1 synapse (let us compare it to the synapse **C-D** in figure 4) in the hippocampus. This means that there is a semblance of arrival of action potential at the presynaptic terminal from a CA3 neuron (let us name this CA3 neuron as **Z**).

2. What does it mean by saying that neuron **Z** is depolarized? Neuron **Z** can only be depolarized by activating a set of axonal terminals of the granule neurons that synapse to the dendritic spines (postsynapses) on the dendritic tree of CA3 neuron **Z**. We really don't know which of the nearly 4×10^4 presynaptic terminals of the neuron **Z** are fired (we know that spatial summation of EPSP from nearly 40 or temporal summation of EPSP much less than 40 postsynapses at the soma can trigger an action potential). Therefore, it is possible that activity from a multitude of possible combinations of inputs

arriving to **Z**'s nearly 4×10^4 dendritic spines from the granule neurons has the capability to trigger the same action potential. This set of all the combinations of granule neurons [**Y**] is determined from the existing synaptic connections that they make with the CA3 neuron **Z**.

3. Similarly, each of the granule neuron synapsing on the neuron **Z** in turn receives synaptic connections from a set of all the possible combinations of entorhinal neurons [**X**]. The set of neurons at the preceding orders that can be similarly determined by moving in a retrograde fashion towards the sensory level.

4. The last step of this process is to determine the sensory receptor location map from the final set neurons derived from both synaptic and network semblances.

5. Once the sensory receptor location map from each synaptic and network semblance is made, they are superimposed to obtain the overlapping sensory receptor location map. From this, the specific identity of the retrieved memory can be derived (Figs.8, 9, and 10).

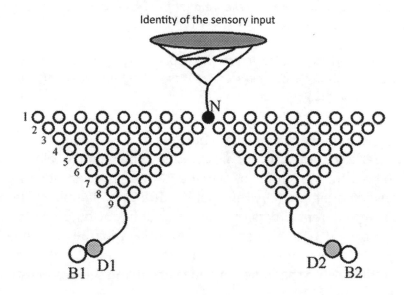

*Figure 8. An illustration of synaptic semblance at one synapse. The larger circles marked **B1**, **D1**, **B2** and **D2** are postsynapses. All other small circles represent neurons. Once activated through the functional LINK, semblance of activity occurs at one postsynapse (from all the possible neurons that can naturally activate that postsynapse). Cue stimulus activates **B1** and **B2**. The EPSPs from them spread through the functional LINKs to the postsynapses **D1** and **D2** and induce semblance. Note that the semblance from **D1** and **D2** in neuronal order 1 overlaps at the neuron **N**. The net semblance is represented by the nature and specificity of the sensory input that is capable of activating the neuron **N**. The overlapping of semblance from more functional LINKs, above a certain threshold value, provides enough strength of semblance for memory. The numbers on the left-hand side represent the order of neurons from the sensory endings towards the higher orders.*

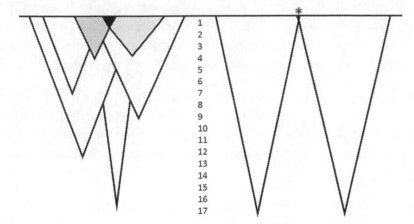

Figure 9. The formation of specific sensory features of memory from semblances occurring at various neuronal orders. The numbers in the middle represent the order of neurons from the sensory endings towards the higher orders.

Left side of the figure shows formation of semblance from multiple orders of neurons. The darkness of the shade represents overlapping of the semblances that determine the identity of the sensation. The darkest triangular area represents the net semblance which in turn determines the identity of the sensory stimulus memorized. Note that the weight of semblance occurring at the higher order of neurons will be different than that occurring at the lower levels.

Right side of the figure shows the overlap of semblances occurring at higher orders of neurons (marked by an asterisk). This overlap of the semblances occurring at higher orders of neurons may provide specificity to the sensory identity (see section VI.9).

6. Semblance formation takes place when the cue stimulus from different sensations reactivates the functional LINKs. A combination of all the sensory maps obtained from each of them will determine sensory identity of the item retrieved during memory retrieval (Fig.10). Since semblance formation takes place at different orders of neurons at different time points, the net semblance formed will be resulting from integrating all the semblances occurring at different orders of neurons resulting in a multi-dimensional sensory product. Note that time is a dimension in this integration step.

7. This process that brings together different aspects of an object/event, such as its shape, color, movement, and other sensor modalities can be seen as equivalent to the process of "binding" (122).

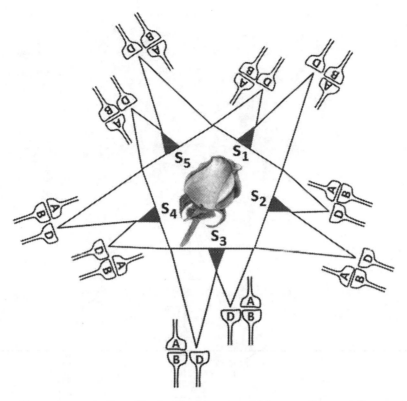

Figure 10.Schematic representation illustrating how semblances formed for each sensation get summated to get the net semblance for the sensory identity of the item to be retrieved. When the cue stimulus for "Rose" arrives, semblances for different sensations are formed. This includes color (vision), softness (touch), odor (smell) etc. Pain from the thorns and the taste of the petals if one has chewed them before, are also considered as part of the sensory identities that are retrieved. S_1, S_2, S_3, S_4 and S_5 represent semblances occurring at each sensory system level.

8. As the cue stimulus pass through the higher neuronal orders, the net semblance starts building. The specific temporal pattern of activation of the neurons in the nervous system (due to synaptic delay) induce multi-dimensional (where time is a dimension) net semblance that represents the sensory features of virtual sensation of memory (Fig.11). In addition, the multi-dimensional integration of semblances taking place at different orders of neurons at different time points provides infinite possible permutations of semblances making the operation of the system non-saturable.

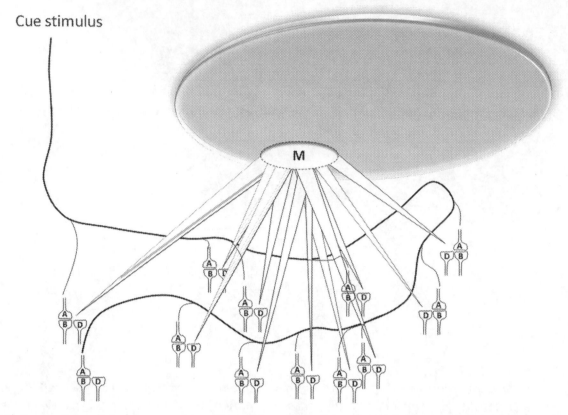

Cue stimulus

*Figure 11. Schematic representation illustrating multi-dimensional integration of semblances. A cue stimulus is shown activating the presynaptic terminal **A** of many synapses in one order of neurons. The EPSPs spread from the postsynapse **B** through the functional LINK to the postsynapse **D**. Semblance is formed at the postsynapse **D**. The sensory representations from all the synaptic semblances are integrated and the overlapping area is shown as **M** representing M-semblance for memory. The large gray coloured circle represents all possible semblances that one nervous system can form at a given time-point.*

Network semblances and semblances from different orders of neurons are not shown in this figure due the expected complexity. From the temporal nature of the semblance formation at different neuronal orders due to normal synaptic delay, time needs to be treated as a dimension. Dimension of time need to be integrated with the semblances to understand the nature of M-semblance for memory.

In wakeful state, background sensory inputs and oscillating neuronal activities activate the nervous system continuously. In a network of neurons that receives a continuum of inputs, instantaneous activation of a specific subset of postsynapses (through the functional LINKs) at different orders of neurons will induce semblance of a sensory input that the specific subset of postsynapses represent leading to memory.

II.5 Hallucinations from neuronal activation – A strong support for semblance

Semblance hypothesis was derived based on the fact that memory is a virtual sensation of a sensory stimulus. In this regard, memory has similar mechanism as that of the hallucinations. Electrical stimulation of the human medial temporal lobe elicits complex visual and auditory hallucinations.

Stimulations of the hippocampus and amygdala were reported to induce complex visual hallucinations (157). In another work, stimulation of the hippocampus and higher-order neocortical sensory-processing areas caused auditory and visual hallucinations (109, 133). These experiments were carried out by blind stimulations. How can such stimulations produce hallucinations of different items? According to the semblance hypothesis, electric stimulation at a blind point at areas of convergence of sensory inputs can activate many islets of LINKed postsynapses at or above the neuronal orders from the point of stimulation leading to net semblances causing hallucinations.

The formation of semblances that can give rise to hallucination while stimulating a blind spot within the hippocampus can be explained in detail by the following cartoon in figure 12. The stimulation of a specific location within an area of convergence is likely to induce many semblances. However, it is likely that at a location of stimulation where one of the semblances produced has comparatively larger strength than others can provide semblances of a single item.

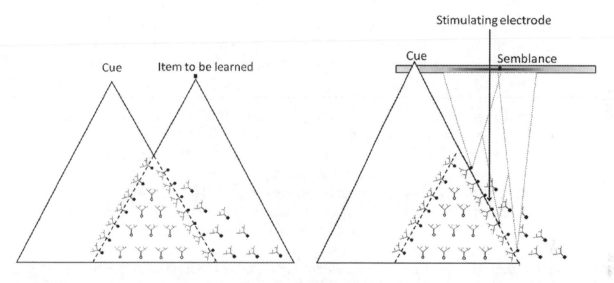

Figure 12. Schematic representation of a mechanism of sensory hallucination during electrical stimulation at areas of convergence of sensory inputs.

Left: Changes during learning showing three types of neurons that are activated. Only a two dimensional representation is given. Neurons with round dark soma can be activated by the cue stimulus alone. They are seen at regions of convergence of the cue and the learned item. Neurons with open round soma are activated only with inputs from both the cue and the learned item. Neurons with filled square soma belong to the learned item and can be activated by the cue stimulus alone, after learning (and not before learning). They are the neurons that belong to the partial networks activated by the cue stimulus as explained in figure 7.

Right: Either the cue stimulus alone or the local stimulation by an electrode can evoke semblances for the learned item. The asterisk denotes a possible location where stimulation by an electrode tip may give rise to visual hallucination of an item similar that of the item whose memory is expected to be retrieved.

II.6 Qualified postsynaptic events that can mark retrieval

Since sensory stimuli from the learned item are not present during retrieval, some postsynaptic events at the synapses belonging to the learned item that can signal the activation of their presynaptic terminal should take place in order to evoke a virtual sensation of the sensory stimuli from the learned item. What post-synaptic cellular event is an equivalent cellular change marking the arrival of an action potential at its presynaptic terminal? At the synaptic level, the induction of a cellular change in the postsynaptic membrane reminiscent of the arrival of an action potential at its presynaptic terminal should be sufficient to induce synaptic semblance. The following are taken as possible postsynaptic events that can induce semblance.

1. For the purpose of derivation of the semblance hypothesis, EPSP reaching at the postsynaptic membrane is used as the standard change equivalent to the arrival of an action potential at its presynaptic terminal. EPSP is viewed as the valid postsynaptic change, since the induced EPSPs can summate to evoke an action potential at the axon hillock of the neuron which can propagate to the higher orders of neurons. This has the advantage of inducing both synaptic and network semblances.

2. Normally, an action potential reaching a presynaptic terminal depolarizes its postsynaptic membrane and leads to a sequence of ionic changes at the shared extracellular matrix (ECM). Sensing these sequential ionic changes that occur in the shared ECM by some membrane proteins on the postsynaptic membrane of a nearby synapse may provide the cellular hallucination of an action potential reaching the latter's presynaptic terminal. In other words, sensing of the sequence of ionic changes in the ECM, normally produced by the arrival of and action potential at the presynaptic terminal, by the postsynaptic membrane is equivalent to an action potential reaching its corresponding presynaptic terminal. This mechanism can only give rise to synaptic semblance and will not lead to network semblance, since it does not lead to the generation of EPSP at the postsynapses of synapses belong to/represent the learned item. In this context, perineural nets that were reported to have a role in memory formation (44) may have a role in inducing ECM effects in inducing semblance.

    As we move towards the intracellular structural and globular proteins, suitability of their roles in inducing semblance decreases due to a) increased non-specific activations of these proteins by mechanisms other than the arrival of action potential at the presynaptic membranes b) reduced chance of meeting the physiological time-scales of retrieval and c) inability to propagate the changes to the downstream neurons at physiological time-scales.

II.7 Extracellular matrix effect

An alternative mechanism for functional LINK formation between the postsynaptic membranes of synapses can occur through an ionic mechanism through the common extracellular matrix (ECM) between them (Fig.13). Both theoretical and laboratory studies have shown that changes in extracellular ionic composition brought about by the activation of one neuron can influence another one in its immediate vicinity (33, 64). During large population spikes in the hippocampus, field effect depolarizations of approximately one-half the population spike amplitude are produced in non-firing pyramidal neurons (135). Neuronal activity increases extracellular potassium ion concentration (32, 103) and decreases extracellular calcium ion concentration (42, 102). Reducing the extracellular calcium ion concentration increases membrane excitability (132). It is likely that co-activation of postsynapses around a common ECM may have evolved innate ion-exchange capabilities. During memory retrieval, activity-induced extracellular accumulation of potassium ions by one postsynapse around the common ECM induces depolarization or other changes in the postsynapses in its vicinity that can induce synaptic semblance.

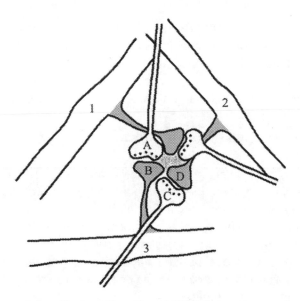

Figure 13. Extracellular matrix effect on functional LINK formation and reactivation. Postsynapses (dendritic spines) **B** *and* **D** *from two different dendrites (numbered 3 and 2) possibly belonging to two different neurons are located around the common extracellular matrix space. Note the close spatial arrangement of the postsynaptic membranes.*

Reduced ECM volume fraction is reported to be a contributory factor for electrical field effects (135) and it is likely to reduce the current required to charge the membrane capacitor and drive the membrane potential to the threshold level. It is also reported that surrounding ECM electrical features may contribute to the generator potentials at sub-thresholds for action potential generation (64).

II.8 Possible types of functional LINKs at the postsynaptic membranes

Three different types of functional LINKs at the postsynaptic membranes of synapses can be formed. They are named as a) Function-Function (F→F) LINKs b) Function-Structure-Function (F→S→F) LINKs and c) Structure-Function (S→F) LINKs.

II.8.1 Function-Function (F→F) LINKs

Changes that occur at the locations where stimuli arrive from the cue and the item to be learned will induce transient changes inducing functional LINKs (Fig.3). Different candidate molecules at the postsynaptic membrane can be involved in initiating the formation of the functional LINKs. From previous experimental studies it can be assumed that N-methyl-D-aspartate (NMDA) receptor functions, oxygenation status, blood glucose levels, dopamine and metabolic state of the neurons (56, 114, 149) can influence the formation of the functional LINKs. Electron microscopic (EM) images often show negligible ECM space between the dendritic spines belonging to different neurons as opposed to the distinct single dendritic spines belonging to the same neuron observed by routine Golgi staining. This indicates that dendritic spines from different neurons are closely apposed to each other. Therefore, closely placed postsynapses belonging to different neurons have the potential to form functional LINKs. This becomes particularly important at locations of convergence of sensory inputs, for example, hippocampus.

In addition, the role of the shared ionic pool at the ECM between the postsynapses during their co-activation is also considered. Neuronal activity increases extracellular potassium concentration (32, 103) and decreases extracellular calcium concentration (42, 102). The latter can increase membrane excitability (132). It is also possible to generate functional LINKs at the common ECM location, by the spread of ionic changes through extracellular ionic acceptor/donor molecules.

II.8.2 Function-Structure-Function (F→S→F) LINKs

Some of the (F→F) LINKs may get converted to (F→S) LINKs after many repetitions of learning. These may be named (F→S→F) LINKs. For example, the dependency of the formation of the (F→F) LINKs on limiting factors gradually reduces and they may function as near-structural LINKs. Repetition of learning may be a factor that determines gradual transformation of the functional LINKs to structural LINKs. Long-lasting memory after one learning trial may operate by this method. Even though these are named as structural LINKs, they should be seen only as near-structural LINKs. Possible mechanism like inductive depolarization where depolarization can be transferred to a neighbouring postsynapse is also considered as an additional mechanism.

II.8.3 Structure-Function (S→F) LINKs

Electron microscopic studies have shown that the hippocampal CA3 dendrites have unusual spines with 1 to 16 spine heads (4, 14) and are called thorny excrescences (38, 46, 97). Specifically, thorny excrescences made up of more than thirty individual spine heads have been identified (10). Since there is no conclusive evidence to suggest that these multiple postsynaptic membrane segments are synapsing on to a single bouton (presynaptic terminal), it can be assumed that many presynaptic terminals are synapsing on to them.

It is possible that many presynaptic terminals synapse on to the postsynaptic membrane segments on a single dendritic spine neck. These postsynaptic membrane segments may not have any functional connections in the beginning. During learning, inputs reaching the presynaptic terminals from the cue and the learned item can cause the co-activation of specific postsynaptic membrane segments and functionally LINK them. These functionally LINKed postsynaptic segments were called shared postsynapses in the initial hypothesis (150).

To begin with, postsynaptic membrane segments are functionally independent due to the presence of a surrounding resistant membrane. During coincident activation of two presynaptic terminals **A** (from the cue) and **C** (from the learning item), a functional LINK is established between the terminals' corresponding postsynaptic membrane segments **B** and **D** by inducing changes in the intervening membrane zone. Therefore, the early functional LINKs can be established only where the corresponding postsynaptic membrane segments are physically close. Repetition of learning can bring simultaneously activated postsynaptic membrane segments closer. During retrieval when EPSP-spread occurs between functionally LINKed postsynaptic membrane segments, the summated (spatial and/or temporal) EPSPs from them activate the same neuron.

Thorny excrescences were reported to show changes after memory tests (140). Sharing of the same postsynaptic membrane by multiple presynaptic terminals is also observed in complex spines in the cerebral cortex (66, 97), cortico-thalamic projections (55), and cerebellum (85). Since the usual thickness of the sections used for electron microscopy is 5×10^{-8} m, it is difficult to identify (S→F) LINKs between the postsynapses of sizes larger than 5×10^{-6} m. Proposed large reconstruction studies (50) may provide more information in the future.

II.9 Expanding islets of functional LINKs

Initially, there are functionally isolated islets of postsynaptic membranes. As more postsynapses get functionally LINKed, the islets of LINKed postsynapses continue to expand (Fig.5). Incremental learning cause gradual expansion of the islets of functional LINKs. Novel learning will induce LINKs between independent postsynapses or between an independent postsynapse and a postsynapse which is part of an islet of functionally LINKed postsynapses or the postsynapses that belong to different islets of postsynapses. Over time, commonly used postsynapses may move towards the center of an islet. This facilitates maintenance of all their functional LINKs. The rarely used postsynapses may move towards the periphery of the islets as some of the functional LINKs get deactivated. Complete disuse of a functional LINK can eventually result in functional separation of a postsynaptic membrane from an islet. Misconnections (mis-LINKs) occurring between islets of LINKed postsynapses that are not functionally LINKed by associative learning cause semblance of abnormal sensory perception leading to chronic sensory disease states that are explained in the discussion section IV.9).

During retrieval, dendritic EPSP from one postsynaptic membrane spreads to the neighbouring ones in an islet of functionally LINKed postsynapses contributes to the latter's ability to induce semblance and also provides EPSPs that can be summated towards eliciting an action potential at the axon hillock of one/more postsynaptic neurons. Action potential generation will depend on the spatial and/or temporal summation of EPSPs generated at the postsynapses by the spread of activity through the functional LINKs. Action potentials generated in this manner, in a group of neurons that belong to the learned item can lead to simultaneous network semblance (see section II.4, stage I.19).

Immediately after learning, a strong semblance occurs in the presence of the cue and can provide more accurate memory. However, remodelling of the axons and dendrites takes place throughout life (24, 166), destabilizing some of the established functional LINKs and the elicitable semblances over time. This becomes particularly important when dendritic spine changes occur on a time-scale of minutes (82, 112), possibly disturbing the relations between some of the newly formed functionally LINKed postsynapses. New related learning events will expand an islet of LINKed postsynapses and will reduce the specificity of semblance achieved from prior learning events through LINKed postsynapses. An expanding islet of postsynapses can increase the sensitivity of related cues to eliciting semblance at different neuronal orders. Specific cue features elicit net functional semblance for specific features of the memorized item, by varying combinations and permutations of semblances occurring at the postsynapses within the islets in different orders of neurons.

II.10 Semblance from islets of functional LINKs

The derivation of semblance (section II.4, stage I.14) has only taken into account the formation of semblances from individual postsynapses. Since the EPSP developed at one postsynapse spreads to the functionally LINKed neighbouring postsynapses in an islet of LINKed postsynapses, semblances will occur at those postsynapses where EPSP reaches. If the cue is highly specific for a learning that had previously occurred, then the net semblance formed from the cue-specific LINKs at different orders of neurons will provide a unique net semblance for memory. As the cue specificity decreases, the probability of the formation of a single effective net semblance will decrease. This may also be viewed as an evolutionary advantage that provides the animal with opportunities to make choices particularly when exposed to cues that were not associatively learned previously. As the cue specificity reach below a certain level, it can evoke more than one net semblance of equal strengths to choose from. Choosing one from more than one semblance can be viewed as a probability problem similar to that in quantum mechanics (Fig.15).

II.11 fMRI and FDG-PET signals – Relationship with functional LINKs

One of the possible determinants of the functional LINKs is the organization of molecules required for its formation or re-activation. Two potential candidates that are associated with functional LINKs are activity-related oxygenation and glucose requirements. Blood oxygenation level dependent (BOLD) signals are observed in specific brain locations in fMRI studies both during learning and memory retrieval (16, 67, 167). In studies seeking to identify neuronal correlates of fMRI signals, extracellular recordings were done along with fMRI studies. The signals used low-impedance extracellular microelectrodes which are low-pass filtered and cut off at nearly 300 Hz to remove the quick fluctuations in the potential difference caused by inward and outward currents of the action potentials. The remaining slower fluctuations that are believed to be post-synaptic potentials, namely local field potentials (LFPs) represent synchronized input into the observed area. LFPs were shown to correlate with the BOLD signals of the fMRI, indicating that the BOLD signals are more closely coupled to synaptic activity representative of the input and intra-cortical processing and not spiking activity (77, 78, 158).

Since fMRI study showed the positive neurovascular coupling takes place with a lag of four to five seconds (98), it indicates that neuronal firing occur initially followed by oxygen release nearly five seconds after that. Thus, it can be generalized that there is a post-learning (post functional LINK formation) and post-retrieval (post-functional LINK re-activation) oxygenation requirement visible as BOLD signals most probably replenishing oxygen that was consumed during learning or retrieval-related synaptic changes. Since learning or retrieval can occur continuously, there are two possibilities. First, from a cellular reserve oxygen is directly used for the functional LINK formation. Second, metabolic pathways like oxidative phosphorylation occur to replenish the high energy molecules used up during the functional LINK formation. In either case, the synaptic activity takes place using a reserve of a reusable substrate, oxygen either to oxygenate some molecules or to use in oxygen for oxidative phosphorylation reactions. In either condition, we can conclude that the functional LINK formation between the postsynapses is an oxygenation-state dependent process and is referred as oxygenation- state dependent functional LINKs in the book.

The hippocampus and amygdala are the primary areas of the brain where sensory inputs from different sensory systems reach (5, 26). These areas have shown increased BOLD signals during both learning and memory retrieval (16, 67, 167). One possibility is that oxygenation of some of the molecules increase EPSP-spread between the postsynaptic membranes of the postsynapses belonging to the cue and the learned item. It is likely that the level of oxygen-dependency for functional LINKs is lower at regions where associative learning of basic survival responses is associated with appropriate environmental cues or sensory inputs. This may be relevant in instances where learning can occur with fewer trials. It may be possible that in some locations of the brain, functional LINKs established after the initial learning become lesser oxygen-dependent during repetitive learning or retrieval. It is also possible that some of the (F→F) LINKs may become completely oxygenation-state independent.

During the learning and memory retrieval events, increased fMRI signal intensities are often visible at the hippocampus. Hippocampus receives sensory inputs from all the sensory systems. Almost all sensory inputs reach at the hippocampus that will result in the reactivation of the already formed functional LINKs. In addition, during new learning there will be formation of new functional LINKs. The higher density of active functional LINKs in a small area will cause increased oxygen release/unit area which in turn result in increased fMRI signal intensity in the hippocampus (and also other regions of sensory convergence like amygdale). If isolated synapses are involved during learning and retrieval, as occurs outside the hippocampus (mainly in the cortex), then the oxygen release occurring at a small volume of brain tissue may not be sufficient to be visible as increased fMRI signals.

Temporo-parietal hypo-metabolism on fludeoxyglucose (^{18}F) - positron emission tomography (18F-FDG PET) is commonly being used as a measure of cognitive defects in Alzheimer's disease. FDG-PET has been used to predict the progression of mild cognitive impairment to Alzheimer's disease (54). Multiple studies have shown that glucose metabolism and blood flow are impaired in the temporo-parietal association cortices (53). In addition, recent human studies have shown direct correlation between FDG-PET signals and memory function (68, 91). It is possible that functioning of the proposed functional LINKs between the postsynapses depends on glucose metabolism similar to that of the oxygen utilization.

II.12 Semblance - Projection to the sensory endings

What does semblances occurring at a synapse mean? How does it help to retrieve memories? In order to understand it, we should be able to identify what basic units that it can contribute towards the formation of virtual sensation of a sensory stimulus during memory retrieval. Semblance formed at one synapse has a sensory identity that can be mapped based on the number of synaptic inputs that each neuron receives (see stage 2 of the derivation in section II.4). If one neuron receives inputs from very large number of neurons in the penultimate neuronal order, then semblance of sensory input will take place from a very large sensory area.

When calculating the semblance, projection is always done towards the sensory nerve endings to estimate the sensory identity of the retrieved memory. When projections are made, it may be important to take into account the inferences from recent experimental results that showed that the nearby neurons with similar orientation tuning showed no correlated activity indicating that adjacent neurons share only a few percent of their inputs (30). This study using recordings from the visual cortex suggests that adjacent neurons share only a few percentages of their inputs or that their activities are uncorrelated. This indicates either of the following. 1) Each neuron may be receiving its inputs mainly from one neuron of the penultimate neuronal order. 2) The nearly 3-4x10^4 synaptic inputs come from very large number of penultimate neurons such that no single penultimate neuron has sufficient output connections to the neuron for eliciting an action potential. Computational studies parallel to the experimental work may bring more information in the near future.

II.13 Semblance at an instantaneous time point

Synaptic semblance from any postsynapse can be extrapolated to obtain the nature of the sensory input based on the activated functional LINKs occurring at the synapses of the higher orders of neurons from the synapse of interest where the first synaptic semblance occurs during memory retrieval (being the first site of convergence of two sensory items where the first functional LINK was formed). All the semblances occurring at the LINKed postsynapses can be used for the net semblance calculated based on the principle of transferability (see section III.5). i. e synaptic semblance from one synapse can be used for computing the sensory identity of the item to be retrieved provided the cue can depolarize the postsynapses through the functional LINKs. Nature of the semblance occurring at four different conditions is explained here.

> *A) At the time of learning:* Many functional LINKs will be formed. They remain functional immediately after learning enabling spread of EPSP through them inducing semblances resulting in working memory.

> *B) After few new learning sessions:* The new learning can be related or completely unrelated. The new related learning under study can re-activate many of the functional LINKs activated by the previous learning. New related learning can also induce new functional LINKs. In other words, due to related learning events, when retrieval of the memory under study activates a postsynapse that lead to semblance, it can increase the sensory area of synaptic semblance (area of sensory endings that can activate postsynapse D, Fig.8). The increase in sensory area (the expansion of sensory location) is proportional to the sensory stimuli by different learning that activate a specific functional LINK at a neuronal order under study.

> *C) Without repetition of the learning or any related learning*: This will lead to three main different types of changes. 1) Some of the newly formed functional LINKs that uniquely represent the learning will loss its ability to get re-activated. In other words they become functionless. 2) Some functional LINKs will be activated by completely novel learning. This is based on the property of transferability as explained in section. III.5. 3). Some functional LINKs will be reactivated by retrieval of memories of the previously learned items.

> *D) Without repetition of the learning and with addition of new neurons:* Incorporation of new neurons in the circuitry can lead to formation of additional semblances that can act as a factor that distorts the net semblance reducing memory, provided there is no repetition of learning. This leads to forgetting over time.

> *E) With repetition of learning under study:* 1) Without new neuron formation: The efficiency of this for memory retrieval depends on the number of

functional LINKs that remain LINKable after the initial learning. The re-activation of these functional LINKs during memory retrieval can reinforce them and aid in strengthening memories. The efficacy of future retrieval depends on the novelty of the first learning which will determine the number of new functional LINKs that need to be reactivated for memory retrieval. It also depends on how sooner the new learning is going to get retrieved. 2) With new neuron formation: This is achieved by repetition of learning at optimal intervals that can incorporate the new neurons. Here, the number of postsynapses where semblances occurs increases. Therefore, during memory retrieval, a strong net semblance for memory can be achieved that contribute to increase the memory.

II.14 Semblance does not require the neuronal orders bridging to the sensory endings

One of the characteristic features of the mechanism for memory retrieval is the formation of semblance which induces the virtual sensation of the sensory stimulus which is memory. Semblance can operate in the absence of the neuronal orders through which the sensory inputs travelled to reach the postsynapses (lower order neurons) where functional LINKs were formed. This is taken as a fundamental property of a nervous system that receives a continuum of sensory inputs. An application of this is seen in the phantom limb phenomenon.

II.15 Presence of a dynamic transient memory code

During memory retrieval, the cue stimulus activity propagates through different orders of neurons. First, note that there is a temporal order of activation of synapses. So, we can say that *permutation* of a set of postsynapses that are activated needs to be calculated as activity spread from initial neuronal order to the higher orders. Due to the synaptic addition, deletion, and neurogenesis, sequences in the *permutation* of the sets of postsynapses will keep changing. Some values in the sequence will be lost or replaced or new sequences are added. At each order of neuron, it is likely that the synapses will get activated together. So, we can say that *combination* of a set of postsynapses activated needs to be calculated at those points.

As explained in the hypothesis derivation, both the synaptic and network semblances are used to assess the net semblance that characterizes the item to be memorized. Each memory has a labile code consisting of the subset of postsynapses and neuronal networks belonging/represent the learned item that are activated during memory retrieval, out of the set of postsynapses and neuronal networks that were co-activated with the cue during learning. This code can be used for computing the identity of the retrieved memory.

In summary,

1.   The semblance code is the set of postsynapses, activated by the cue, representing the learned item.

2.   The code will be different for different cues.

3. The code induced by a given specific cue will keep fluctuating from time to time due to synapse addition, elimination and neurogenesis. The expected changes due to this are very minimal.

A typical code may be represented as in figure 14. For the retrieval of a specific memory, there will be a minimum cue requirement. Similarly, there will be a maximum. Improving the cue further may not change the qualities of the item retrieved for a given nervous system for a given amount of prior learning that it had undergone.

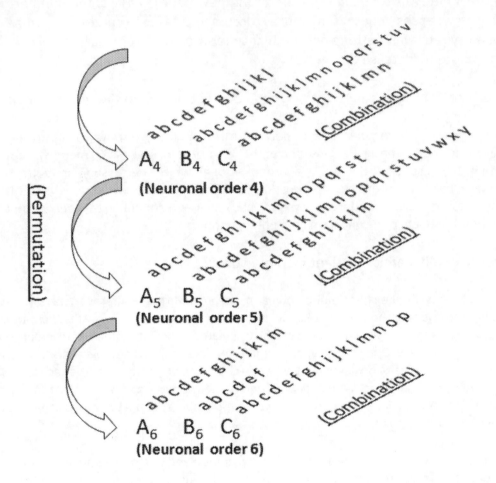

Figure 14. Transient memory code at a given time point. The numbered capital letters A,B,C denotes different neuronal orders. The small letter a,b,c,d etc. denote different neurons of a given neuronal order. Activation of the postsynapses at a to l, a to v, and a to n on the top row takes place almost at the same time. The semblance from them can be calculated as a combination product. In contrast, if we look at the first column of postsynapses in each neuronal order (a to l, a to t and a to m), they get activated in a temporal fashion. The semblance from them can be calculated as a permutation product as it has a specific order of occurrence. The net functional semblance is obtained by integrating the combination and permutation of semblances. Note that time is a dimension that gets incorporated within the permutation product. The memory code shows very minimal changes over time due to addition and deletion of synapses and the effect of new neurons into the circuitry.

II.16 Types of net semblances

Semblances can be broadly classified into three major types – primary, secondary and tertiary.

Primary semblances: All primary sensory modalities - color, sound, smell, touch, taste and pain have characteristic primary semblances. Primary semblances may also exist for consciousness and qualia and may be named as C-semblance and Q-semblance respectively. The configuration of the primary semblances is a function of the complexity of the nervous system. It is likely that the primary semblances are determined by the genetic make up of the animal, are evolutionarily attained and likely to be constant for a species.

Secondary semblances: In contrast to the primary semblances, secondary semblances depend on the specificity of the cue stimulus used in an associative learning. Depending on the specificity of the cue and the functional LINKs formed by the previous learning, specific net semblances form during memory retrieval. Examples of secondary semblances include memory and path finding.

Tertiary semblances: They can occur when a completely novel cue stimulus is presented to a nervous system that has associatively learned many items in the past. The nervous system will use the properties of combinations, permutations and transferability properties to induce a net semblance as a response to this novel cue stimulus. The novel cue may produce one or more than one net semblances (Fig.15). The nervous system can test these semblances against the available sensory data at the moment, one of the requirements for a memory storage mechanism (1). An example is an acute response-requiring condition where the nervous system is exposed to a novel cue. Here, the nervous system gets a selection pressure to choose one semblance from a few. This now becomes a probability problem similar to the quantum indeterminacy.

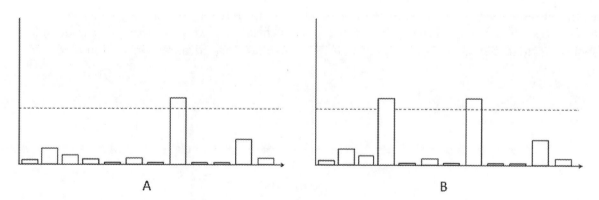

A　　　　　　　　　　　　B

Figure 15. Graphical representation of the weight of net M-semblances (Fig.11) formed by a cue stimulus. The bars represent different net semblances. The horizontal dotted line represents the threshold below which the net semblances do not lead to memory.

Figure A: When the net semblance is above a certain threshold, it will evoke a virtual sensation of a sensory stimulus which is memory. This is shown as a single bar that is shown above a horizontal dotted line which represents the threshold.

Figure B: A novel cue may produce more than one net semblance. If they have equal values of strength the nervous system will veto against other sensory evidences as explained in section V.9. In an acute response requiring situation, choosing one from two semblances of equal strengths will become a probability problem similar to that in quantum indeterminancy (section II.10).

The nature of semblances depends on the amount of associative learning done by the nervous system in the past. In a nervous system that has done more learning, some of the peak net semblances formed from novel cues provide abilities to form intuitions, creative ideas etc. The same principle can be applied in the development of intelligent machines and is discussed in section X.

II.17 Excitatory and inhibitory neurotransmission

Synapses with different excitatory neurotransmitters will be taking part in the formation of functional LINKs. Gama amino butyric acid-releasing (GABAnergic) cell types regulate temporal dynamics of synaptic activity at different locations on a neuron and in a neuronal network (62). When computing the net semblance, these activities need to be taken into account.

II.18 Non-specific semblance

For the purpose of derivation of the hypothesis, we used synaptic semblance as semblance formation from single synapses. As the postsynapses within an islet of LINKed postsynapse are functionally LINKed, EPSP can spread between the LINKed postsynapses and induce semblance at all those synapses depending on the extent of the EPSP-spread. Even though the spread of EPSPs across the islet increases the non-specific semblance at that specific islet of LINKed postsynapses level, it will become insignificant when computation of semblances from all the neuronal orders is done. Thus, it will not affect the formation of final specific semblance required for the specific memory retrieval in the presence of a specific cue.

The non-specific activation of the functionally LINKed postsynapses in an islet provides opportunities to the nervous system to develop tertiary semblances for novel responses without the need for any previous associative learning. The advantage of such a possible mechanism is discussed at later sections (see tertiary semblance in section II.16 and evolutionary advantage in section XI.5).

III. Examination of the hypothesis in different physiological conditions

The premises that the LINKed postsynapses can be formed during associative learning and they can induce semblance of activity from the presynaptic terminals of the learned item during memory retrieval were used to build the hypothesis. Now, it is necessary to examine whether these premises provide support for the conclusions by examining various physiological conditions.

III.1 Plasticity changes

Alterations in the spine shape are enduring structural correlates of synaptic plasticity [review, (76)] and have been reported to accompany learning of various tasks. When two simultaneous sensory inputs reach the postsynapses of the LINKable synapses during learning, a functional LINK forms between them. During related learning events, new postsynapses are functionally LINKed expanding the islet of functionally LINKed postsynapses. If any of the postsynapses in an islet of functional LINKs is repeatedly co-activated in different learning events (see the effect of transferability in section III.5), it may move close to the center of the islet where it will be able to maintain large number of functional LINKs. Those postsynapses and their functional LINKs that are not used may get moved away from the center of an islet of LINKed postsynapses. Repetition of learning may promote dendritic spine mobility to optimize the positioning of the postsynapses and also to achieve stabilization of functional LINKs.

III.2 Disuse reduction of memory

After the initial session of a new learning, the absence of repetitions is likely to result in the withdrawal of many of the newly initiated cellular changes at the functionally LINKed postsynapses (F→F LINKs) (see section II.8.1). This can result in loss of transient functional LINKability at the time of retrieval using the cue stimulus. On the other hand, increased number of repetitions can reduce the threshold requirements for achieving transient functional LINKability and may even convert (F→F) LINKs to (F→S→F) LINKs (see section II.8.2).

III.3 Ease of learning a related task

In a related learning event, one presynaptic terminal (whose postsynaptic membrane is already LINKed with another as a result of previous learning) may become co-activated with different presynaptic terminals (see figure 5). Each new learning event will add new postsynaptic membrane LINKs within postsynaptic islets in an (F→F) LINK. This gives a possible cellular explanation for the ease with which new information can be incorporated in the presence of an associate "schema" for fast system consolidation during related learning (145). It is likely that learning a related task requires less energy expenditure due to preservation of the LINKs between the postsynaptic membranes from the previous learning events. This is in agreement with the positron emission tomographic (PET) results showing that only fewer neural activity is required to process repeated stimuli for memory (139).

III.4 Strength of the cue stimulus

A cue may be a component within a learned task or separate from it. If unrelated learning has occurred using components of the same cue, retrieval of a specific memory may be affected. For perfect retrieval, a specific cue that can reach a specific set of LINKed postsynapses is required. The minimum qualities of a partial cue required to evoke a specific memory will depend on the threshold semblance required from all the neuronal levels. By increasing the depth of the level of processing by elaborating the item to be processed, the nervous system can remember better. This was examined in detail during previous studies (131).

The previous learning events enable functional LINKs to be used transferably. When a major subset of such functional LINK is used in a particular learning or memory retrieval, we refer to them as an associative "schema". Previous study has shown that if an associative "schema" is already created by previous learning, then the consolidation process of the new learning is faster (145). According to semblance hypothesis, pre-existing schemas are an apparent phenomenon and is a function of the specificity of the cue capable of activating specific sets of functional LINKs from the total number of activable functional LINKs.

III.5 Transferability

Some of the brain regions may be used for a large number of learning events. There will be limitations in maintaining large numbers of islets of functional LINKs within a given region. In situations where functional LINKs are limited to few orders of neurons in a particular brain region in a specific learning paradigm, it is likely that some of the established functional LINKs are shared by new related learning. Specific overlapping of the components in different learning involving the same brain region have been shown to contribute to an improvement in performance on untrained tasks (22), indicating the possibility that some of the established functional LINKs are transferable. At a single postsynaptic level, different cue stimuli when pass through the functional LINKs to a specific postsynapse, it induces the same synaptic semblance.

New learning events induce new functional LINKs. These functional LINKs will be re-activated by any sensory input that is capable of activating either postsynapse. Re-activation occurring in this manner will maintain some of these functional LINKs for long time even without repetition of the learning that originally made these LINKs. In summary, majority of the functional LINKs are re-activated by related or unrelated, learning or retrieval events. Thus, maintaining the functional LINKs in a re-activable state allows the nervous system to use them for eliciting semblances during memory retrieval.

III.6 Degeneracy at the LINKed postsynapses

From the derivation of the semblance hypothesis, it can be seen that the functionally LINKed postsynapses at the time of learning need to get re-activated during memory retrieval. Since there is expansion of the functionally LINKed postsynapses during related learning events, spread of EPSP occurs between many of the functionally LINKed postsynapses within an islet of LINKed postsynapses. Therefore, the rules set for defining semblance in the earlier sections need not be strictly restricted to just one pair of synapses. For example, in figure IV, the firing of **A** need not be necessary for the activation of postsynapse **D**, provided postsynapse **D** receives EPSP from a third postsynapse with which it has functional LINKs (see figure V).

As the size of an islet of LINKed postsynapses increases, more and more presynaptic terminals can activate a particular postsynapse due to the spread of EPSP. This results in the degeneracy of the memory code at single LINKed postsynaptic level and provides sensitivity to the retrieval process using features from a related cue. Thus theoretically, degeneracy provides means for retrieving the same sensory item using different cues. The range of EPSP-spread from a depolarizing postsynaptic membrane in a large islet of LINKed postsynapses may vary. Degeneracy can only be applied to those postsynapses within an islet of LINKed postsynapses in which EPSP can spread.

III.7 Input non-specificity for eliciting an action potential

Let us assume that activation of a set A (number 1 to 40) of forty postsynapses (dendritic spines) out of 4×10^4 dendritic spines (average value) on a neuron can induce an action potential at the axon hillock of that neuron. Activation of another set B (number 40 to 80) of forty postsynapses (dendritic spines of the same neuron) can also induce the same action potential and activate the same postsynapses in the islet of LINKed postsynapses. Temporal summation of much lesser than forty synapses belonging to either set A or set B can also elicits the same action potential. These clearly indicate that there is no input specificity for eliciting an action potential.

The action potential will activate all the presynaptic terminals on the axonal endings of that neuron activating the postsynaptic membranes of different islets of functional LINKs. Since the same action potential can be generated by activation of a multitude of different combinations or permutations of postsynapses (dendritic spines) of a neuron, it can be seen that a given functional LINK (at the postsynapses of the synapses at the axonal terminals) can get activated by different sensory inputs.

III.8 Hippocampal circuitry and semblance

The hippocampus receives afferents converging from all cortical association areas (5) that carry information from various sensory stimuli. Due to the convergence of connections from multiple sensations, it is a major site where functional LINKs form and will be used for eliciting semblances during memory retrieval. In addition, transferability of functional LINKs will be utilized during retrieval. These features together can be used to achieve threshold activation for semblance for an item in the presence of a partial cue stimulus. Genetically removing the NR1 subunit of NMDA receptors from the CA3 neurons has failed to retrieve memory using a partial cue (101) indicating that formation of sufficient semblance requires necessary neuronal activity at the CA3 level. It is possible that the neuronal activity at this neuronal order evokes activities at higher neuronal orders that are essential for evoking sufficient net semblance for memory formation.

III.9 Hippocampal neurogenesis

Recent work has shown that new granule neurons are continuously added (57) to the existing granule neurons. It can be expected that these new granule neurons make afferent connections with the entorhinal cortical neurons through the perforant path and efferent connections with the CA3 neurons through the Mossy fiber path. Introducing new granule neurons will have different implications on the net semblance formed for retrieval of memories. Work has shown that newly generated neurons in the adult are not only affected by the formation of a hippocampal-dependent memory, but also participate in it (134).

Patients with medial temporal lobe damage have shown great difficulties in forming new long-term memories (130), indicating that long-term storage of newly learned items requires the formation of new neurons. Based on the present hypothesis, specificity of memories can be retained for longer times with repetition of learning (or of related learning) in the presence of newly formed neurons. Recent work has shown that hippocampal new neurons is not obligatory for memory formation (58). Based on the present hypothesis this can be explained since a) memory is a function of LINK formation between the postsynapses b) net semblance is the net effect of semblances from different neuronal orders, even though we don't know the weight of the semblances from different neuronal orders c) for the above reasons, hippocampal new neurons are not obligatory for memory formation (even though lack of new neurons affect long-term storage. The transferable functional LINKs from previous related learning events can confound the results of the studies.

a) *New neurons and repetition of learning*

Hippocampus is considered as essential for new declarative memory (137). Due to the formation of new neurons and their synapses, repetition of learning introduces new functional LINKs between the postsynapses at the orders of neurons at and above (at higher orders) the granule neuron-CA3 level. Thus, neurogenesis increases the combinations (due to simultaneous occurrence of synaptic semblances at one neuronal order) and permutations (since semblance take place at different times in different neuronal orders due to synaptic delay) of semblances that contribute to the net semblance for memory. Increased number of functional LINKs will provide increased semblance strength facilitating strong memory retrieval.

In short, during retrieval of memory, a previously learned and repeatedly re-learned item will have increased semblances at higher orders of neurons (in the cortex) than a newly learned item during retrieval of memory. The increasing semblances at the higher orders of neurons (in the cortex) will become capable of evoking sufficient memory even in the absence of semblances from the hippocampus. This explains the mechanism behind the consolidation process that can be viewed resulting from a shift of the location of effective semblance formation for a particular memory from the hippocampus to the cortex (Figs.16,17). At one stage in this process, memories are stored both in the hippocampus and in the cortex supporting the suggestion that new declarative memories are stored in the neocortical areas (9, 138) along with the hippocampus.

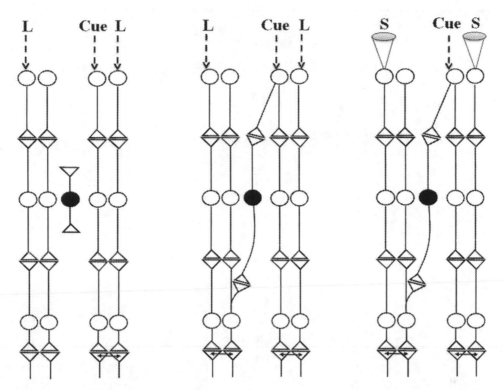

Figure 16 .Schematic representation to explain how new neurons increase semblance and strength of memory by introducing changes at the entorhinal cortex-granule neuron-CA3 neuronal levels. Note that in all the figures there are three neuronal orders in circles (from top to bottom they represent entorhinal cortex-granule neuron-CA3 neurons).

Left panel shows four different neuronal pathways and a new neuron at the granule neuronal order (soma in thick black). There is a functional LINK formed between the right most neuronal orders between the last synapses (between synapses that carry stimuli from the cue and learned item (L)) during learning.

Middle panel shows that the new neuron makes synaptic connections with the neuronal order through which the cue stimulus pass with another neuronal pathway, one of whose postsynapses is close to one of the postsynapses of the neuronal pathway from the item to be learned (L). This allows the formation of a functional LINK to form during repetition of the learning process.

Right panel shows that when the system is exposed to the cue stimulus, both the functional LINKs get re-activated and semblances are formed (which are represented as S).

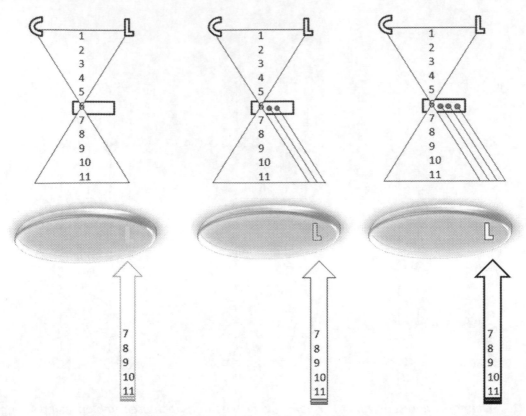

*Figure 17. Schematic representation that shows how new neuron formation at the granule neuron layer increases semblances that contribute to the strength of memory. Note that in all the figures cue and learning stimulus are represented by **C** and **L**. There are eleven neuronal orders starting from the sensory ending. Neuronal order 6 is the granule neuron order where both the cue and learning stimulus shows to converge (represented by conical shape from **C** and **L** to the neuronal order 6). After neuron order 6, the representation is shown to get converged as it reaches neuronal order 11. The round shape represents the total possible semblances of the nervous system. During memory retrieval through semblances at neuronal orders 7 to 11 (see figure 11), net semblance for the learned item is formed (represented by the letter **L** in the net semblance area).*

*Left panel has no new neuron. The semblance for **L** during memory retrieval is weak (represented by light colored letter **L**).*

*Middle panel shows two new neurons. By repeated learning or related learning, the number of functional LINKs at higher neuronal orders increases. This results in increased strength of semblance for **L** during memory retrieval (represented by darker-colored letter **L** than the previous case).*

*Right panel shows three new neurons at the granule neuronal order, further increasing the number of functional LINKs formed at the higher orders of neurons that can contribute to net semblance. The net semblance for **L** during memory retrieval is shown as strong (represented by the bright colored letter **L**).*

b)*Effect of new neurons in the absence of repetition of learning*

If there are no repetitions of learning after the initial learning, neurogenesis will have an adverse effect on memory. New neurons will form new functional LINKs at their dendritic side during unrelated learning. During memory retrieval using the same cue, even though there will be appropriate semblance (provided sufficient functional LINKs that can induce semblances for memory retrieval are active), there will be many extra semblances formed through the functional LINKs that were made during unrelated learning. This will dilute the net semblance and may prevent memory retrieval.

c) *Effect of removal of hippocampus in an adult animal*

Hippocampus is an area of convergence of multiple sensory inputs that leads to the formation of new functional LINKs at the neuronal orders at and above the level of the hippocampus. During hippocampus-dependent learning, specific inputs reach LINKable postsynapses at various orders of neurons spanning from the hippocampus to the cortex. If the hippocampus is removed, cue stimulus can reach the higher order of neurons through the extra-hippocampal connections. If sufficient number of LINKable postsynapses outside the hippocampus remains intact, it allows effective functional semblance for memory in the presence of the cue stimulus. As long as the number of postsynapses where semblance take place exceeds the threshold for effective semblance for memory, retrieval of memory occurs.

What happens if we remove hippocampus once learning has already occurred? The functional LINKs at higher orders of neurons will be able to contribute to specific semblances to retrieve memory for those learned items that can have sufficient semblances at the extra-hippocampal locations. The cue stimulus needs to reach at the higher orders of neurons through alternate routes. Since sufficient functional LINKs are not formed at the higher orders sufficient for net semblance for memory, recent learning will be lost first. The old memories exist since the functional LINKs were maintained by either related learning or by other learning events.

During the interval between the old learning and memory retrievals new neurons are formed. Both repetition of learning and related learning that pass through the new neurons will increase the number of functional LINKs in the cortex.

We have seen In section II.9 that due to continued use of a functional LINK the commonly used postsynapses will get moved towards the center of the islet of postsynapses. This will make the centrally located postsynapse in an islet of functionally LINKed postsynapses to remain stably LINKed for longer duration of time. In the case of recent learning, the new functional LINKs are likely to be at the periphery of a functionally LINKed islet of postsynapses. Lack of reactivation of functional LINKs in the cortex formed during a learning event (since hippocampus is lost) will make these functional LINKs to gradually disappear causing loss of recent memories.

d) *Reduced neurogenesis and pseudo-dementia*

It is known that depression is associated with reduction of neurogenesis in the hippocampus (127). This reduced neurogenesis may contribute to the dementia by reducing the combinations/permutations of semblances from possible functional LINKs at the higher orders of neurons.

III.10 Brain oscillations and network semblance

Mechanisms providing electrical coupling between the pyramidal neurons (27) proposed for generating or modulating neuronal oscillations are not yet known. However, hemodynamic signals were shown to correlate tightly with synchronized gamma oscillations (104). Therefore, it is possible to hypothesize that activity-induced increased blood flow can lead to increased oxygen release close to those active synapses and re-activate the functional LINKs. The EPSPs transmitting through the functional LINKs can lead to lateral spread of neuronal activity. This lateral spread of activity through the LINKed postsynapses may be a possible mechanism for the coupling between the pyramidal neurons (Fig.18). In other words, the spread of activity through the LINKable postsynapses can activate neural ensembles in a synchronized manner producing different brain waves (see section VI.2)

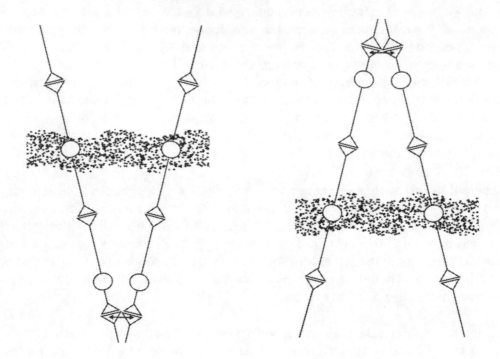

Figure 18. The oscillations of neurons in the hippocampus can lead to re-activation of functional LINKs and visa versa.

Left panel: Oscillations of neurons induce activities from two neurons to reach at the converging synapses at higher orders reactivating the learning-induced functional LINKs. This occurs at many functionally LINKed postsynapses inducing large net semblances. However the net semblance resulting from them won't match with semblances for any of the previously learned items. This non-specific large semblance may contribute to conscious awareness of the environment.

Right panel: At higher orders of neurons from the locations of functional LINK reactivation neurons can get activated provided large number of inputs reach there causing spatial and temporal summations. This leads to an oscillating neuronal activity. This oscillation may become autonomous if there are recurrent connections.

It is possible that neuronal oscillations can activate partial networks inducing network semblances. If there is an order for the activation that mimic a particular learning, then memories can be retrieved as sequences within an episode. Demonstration of theta-rhythmically firing cells in other structures of Papez's circuit (34) may indicate that such rhythmic neuronal activity is important to incorporate time in deriving the multi-dimensional property of the retrieved memories.

Encoding and retrieval should ideally take place in the presence of similar oscillations in order to optimize the activities of the neurons in response to a specific cue stimulus. This will induce activation of appropriate sets of functional LINKs that will induce specific semblance for specific memory retrieval. It is likely that any deviation from the oscillation will incorporate unassociated neurons and result in non-specific synaptic and network semblances. In rats, blocking neural activity in one hippocampus (by injecting tetrodotoxin) prevented them from effectively avoiding regions of the room where foot shock was administered (111). It is likely that activation of uncoupled hippocampal pyramidal neurons induces semblances that are not corresponding to the actual positions contributing to the loss of associative memory. Similarly, in schizophrenia impaired stimulus-induced gamma synchronization in the scalp-recorded EEG was found across neocortical networks (136).

Working memory task is associated with cortical theta oscillations in humans (59, 141) and in rodents (164). Along with the high-frequency firing of inhibitory interneurons, coupling between the axons of pyramidal neurons is important for generating or modulating oscillations (review, (80, 143). Activation of the axons was reported to induce antidromic activation of neighboring axons resulting in somatic spikelet potentials in neurons of hippocampal slices (129). Even though axonal gap junctions were shown to maintain this coupling function (27, 129), experimental evidence is inconclusive. In this context, the role of functionally LINKed postsynapses that may cause lateral spread of EPSPs need to be further explored.

III.11 Sleep and semblance

Based on the present hypothesis, lateral spread of activity through the LINKs is a possible mechanism contributing to the oscillatory brain activity. During sleep different wave patterns form such as REM and NREM sleep cycles occur. As learning and retrieval of memories occur during the wake period, it is possible that the activation of neurons that represent the learned item take place better at the same oscillatory stage as that occurred during learning.

Since waveforms keep changing during sleep, it is likely that the neurons involved in learning during the wake cycle get activated at some stage of the sleep. Any activation of the neurons involved in learning can possibly re-activate the functional LINKs formed during the learning event. This can have two consequences. One, it can convert the (F→F) LINKs to (F→S→F) LINKs and secondly, reduce the oxygenation requirement for the re-activation of the functional LINKs. Since the functional LINKs can be used interchangeably for memory retrieval, it can be said that activity of neurons during different oscillations stabilizes the memory capacity.

III.12 Role of memory retrieval on memory

One study has shown that repeated retrieval induced through testing (and not repeated encoding during additional study) produces large positive effects on long-term retention of memory (60). This indicates that retrieval itself can re-activate the functional LINKs made during learning. In another study, the investigators cued new memories in humans during slow-wave sleep by presenting an odour that had been presented as context during prior learning (120). This re-exposure to the odour improved the retention of hippocampus-dependent declarative memories. How can exposure to the cue alone improve associative memories?

During retrieval of memories at an optimal interval, two events can occur. One, the cue stimulus activate a partial network that belongs to/represent the learned item as explained in figure 7. Two, the cue stimulus, after an optimal interval, activate some of the new granule neurons that have made connections with the entorhinal cortical neurons. These new neurons will activate neurons at the higher order of neurons. Activation of these two neuronal pathways will lead to the formation of new functional LINKs between them. When the cue is presented at a later occasion, it will induce additional semblances at the new functional LINKs formed during the earlier retrieval. This provides the formation of stronger semblance for the item to be retrieved as demonstrated in figure 16. This supports the proposal that upon each occasion of memory retrieval, a new trace may be created by the hippocampus regardless of the memory age (96, 100).

III.13 Place cells

Based on the present hypothesis, the same cue that was used during learning will activate a partial network which is a subset of the neuronal network that was activated by the learned item to elicit partial network semblance (see figure 7). It is possible that place cells (110) are part of the partial network of neurons that are activated by the environmental cues (learned item). It can also explain the recent findings that firing of the same neurons in the hippocampus occur during specific memory recall in humans (43).

III.14 Dopamine and working memory

Dopamine was shown to be important in working memory functions (11, 128), possibly by neuro-modulating the gain within the prefrontal cortical network. However, the exact mechanisms of this are not known. Based on the present hypothesis, it is possible that dopamine may play a role in promoting the formation and stabilization of the functional LINKs.

III.15 Mirror neurons

Most body movements are accompanied by a visual perception of those movements. Muscle movements are associated with activation of sensory receptors of stretch and proprioception. Different associative learning takes place between these receptor activities during muscle movements. One such event is associative learning between the visual stimuli and the sensory fibers activated during the muscle movements. In addition, the sensory drive for the muscle movements will act as a third sensory input that might get LINKed along with the above two. Later, when the visual stimulus is presented (as an animal views another animal carrying out a movement), it acts as a cue. This causes the spread of activity through the functional LINKs and induces activity in several neurons (Figures 5 and 7). It is possible that some of these neurons are mirror neurons.

Visual stimuli can pass through the functional LINKs to the postsynapses transmitting a) sensory stimuli from the muscle movements, and b) sensory inputs for muscle movements. The EPSPs spreading through the latter can activate some of the neurons in the motor cortex resulting in the activity of some of the motor units as reported (Review, (121). An fMRI study has shown that BOLD signals were reduced in mirror neuron areas in autistic people and that the reduction was proportional to the impairment in the subjects (23). Evidence from several studies has shown mirror neuron dysfunction in autism (47, 106, 142) which is associated with motor defects, language and social impairments. Exploring the nature of functional LINKs between the postsynapses may provide us answers to the patho-physiology of this disease.

III.16 Phantom limb

One of the characteristic features of the mechanism for memory retrieval is the formation of semblance which induces the virtual sensation of the sensory stimulus. Semblance can operate in the absence of the neuronal orders through which the sensory inputs had travelled to reach the postsynapses (lower order neurons) to form the functional LINKs. Based on the present hypothesis, this is taken as a fundamental property of a nervous system that receives a continuum of sensory inputs. An indirect application of this can be used to explain the phantom limb phenomenon. Whenever an appropriate cue reaches the brain, perception of the presence of the amputated limb occur leading to the phenomenon of phantom limb. The non-requirement of the physical presence of the limb for its perception explains how semblances can contribute to the virtual sensation.

III.17 Procedural memory

Memories of procedures that are performed using sensory-motor system persist longer than other types of memories. New procedural memories form during learning of coordination of motor activities. Each new procedural learning builds unique functional LINKs essential for its specific memory. Once they are built, maintenance will takes place by unrelated learning or any motor learning that activate those related functional LINKs. Whenever the postsynapses from a pair of sensory inputs are reactivated, their functional LINKs get more strengthened and stabilized. Along with this, partial neuronal network that belongs to the learned item is activated. This network may contribute to the coordinated activities.

IV Plausible explanation for pathological conditions

Clinical disorders of memory may provide us with bits and pieces of information that can help us to understand the mechanism of memory storage. The following facts argue for taking an approach at least to verify whether semblance hypothesis is correct or not. The following situations may be used to explore the mechanism further. 1) Cognitive disorders of unknown pathology are being treated successfully by pharmaceutical agents with known mechanism of action. 2) Known mechanism of action of many pharmacological agents cannot explain how they act to relieve the symptoms in different organic and psychiatric disorders. 3) Improvement or worsening of different types of memories takes place during treatment of different organic diseases of known causes. These conditions may provide opportunities to rigorously test the hypothesis.

IV.1 Hallucinations

Exploring hallucinations may help us to examine the hypothesis further. Out of different hallucinations, visual hallucination is used as an example since hallucinations produced by defects at different orders of visual pathway are present. There are mainly two types of visual hallucinations. Release hallucination resulting from visual loss and ictal hallucination resulting from irritability of the visual cortex. It can be seen from the literature that diseases affecting a group of early orders of neurons induce hallucinations without any specific features. Hallucinations resulting from anterior visual system disorders are typically unformed (99). Here, a group of neurons of the early orders are activated. The net semblance resulting from it will not have any specific net semblance. This can explain hallucinations of simple flashes of light without any specific features. In conditions that lead to irritation of the visual cortical "What area" hallucinations with specific facial features occur. This indicates that the synaptic and network semblances formed from these regions normally produce memories for faces.

By summarizing the findings, it is possible to predict the following features for semblance. 1) Retrieval efficiency after associative learning will be best in the presence of the specific cue that can activate all the orders of neurons that were activated during learning and provide maximum strength for semblance. 2) Content of the hallucinations depends on the site of stimulation. Activating a specific location of the brain, where sensory inputs normally converge can induce semblances causing sensory hallucinations. 3) Stimulating a set of non-specific neurons or a non-specific brain location (where large number of convergence does not take place) will not elicit any semblance for a sensory stimulus.

In summary, quality of semblance is a function of the set of synapses and the partial neuronal network that are activated. Since the dimension of time is a crucial factor that determines the quality of semblance, the type of stimulus occurring in various pathologies that determine the synaptic transmission is an important factor to be considered. The inference from the hypothesis indicates that sensory perception of the semblances either as memory or as hallucinations takes place only if it can form net semblance of sufficient strength above a certain threshold.

In fMRI studies, auditory and visual hallucinations were shown to accompany activation of hippocampus and higher-order neocortical sensory-processing areas (109, 133). Electrical stimulation of the human medial temporal lobe elicits complex visual and auditory hallucinations, whereas stimulations of the amygdala and hippocampus induce complex visual hallucinations (157). According to the semblance hypothesis, electric stimulation at a blind point in areas of convergence of sensory inputs activates many islets of LINKed postsynapses leading to the formation of net semblances causing hallucinations (section II.5).

IV.2 Dementia in Alzheimer's disease

Mutations in amyloid precursor protein (*APP*), presenilin-1 (*PS-1*) and presenilin-2 (*PS-2*) genes produce abnormal protein products that lead to the pathogenesis of Alzheimer's disease. Intracellular neurofibrillary tangles and extracellular amyloid plaques are the two microscopical changes that are observed in Alzheimer's disease. The disease is characterized by regional impairment of cerebral glucose metabolism in neocortical association areas including posterior cingulate, temporo-parietal and frontal multimodal association cortices (53). Based on the present hypothesis, it may be viewed that the functional LINK formations between the postsynapses during learning and their re-activation during memory retrieval are likely affected by the pathological changes observed in Alzheimer's disease.

IV.3 Dementia in Lewy body disease

It is a complex neurological disorder requiring a triad of symptoms of dementia, visual hallucinations and Parkinson's disease to make a probable diagnosis. The treatment of this disease is a challenging one since medications for one symptom may worsen the other symptoms. Here, we try to find an explanation for this paradox by using semblance hypothesis. According to the semblance hypothesis, dementia occurs when functional LINKs formed during learning cannot be actively maintained or re-activated. Visual hallucinations occur when there are pathological mis-LINKs occurring between the islets of post-synapses in regions associated with vision. It is known that Parkinson's disease is caused by reduced DOPA in the substantia gelatinosa neurons projecting to the basal ganglia.

Lewy bodies are intracytoplasmic eosinophilic neuronal inclusions seen in this disease containing the protein alpha-synuclein aggregated with abnormally phophorylated neurofilaments. Lewy bodies may disrupt memory by affecting the formation and re-activation of the functional LINKs. Functionally mis-LINKed islets of postsynapses can induce semblances that can lead to hallucinations which will dilute the net semblance for memory for a specific item.

Whenever Parkinson's symptoms in Lewy body disease are treated with DOPA, it will reactivate pathological functional mis-LINKs between the islets of postsynapses inducing the visual hallucinations. Dopamine is implicated in motivation-induced learning (160). Dopamine may be facilitating functional LINK formation as discussed in section III.14. Whenever visual hallucinations are treated with dopamine receptor antagonists, the symptoms of Parkinson's disease worsen. In either situation, cognitive improvement to achieve the baseline state may not be possible since it won't be possible to bring back pre-existed functional LINKs that are lost during disease process.

IV.4 Dementia in other disorders

In fronto-temporal dementia (FTD) inclusion bodies positive for ubiquitin, a 76 amino acid protein forming part of a cytoplasmic system for degradation and digestion of other intracellular proteins, are seen in the granule neurons of the dentate gyrus. In addition FTD is also associated with mutations in the microtubule associated protein tau (*MAPT*) gene. Accumulation in the brain of an abnormal partially protease-resistant, isoform of a host-encoded glycoprotein known as prion protein (PrP) is seen in Prion disease. It is possible that the above pathological changes affect both the a) formation of the LINKs during learning and b) re-activation of the functional LINKs during memory retrieval.

IV.5 Changes due to hypoxia

Patients with congestive cardiac failures and respiratory disorders who cannot maintain adequate oxygen saturation in their blood can have defects in their memory (159). It could be either a) due to reduced availability of oxygen for oxygenation state dependent functional LINK formation or b) due to the reduced production of ATP required for the active process of functional LINK formation and its reactivation.

IV.6 Wide-spread storage of memory

Lesions of the structures of Papez's circuit have shown memory defects (156). In addition, a number of interconnected cerebral regions that are associated with the regions of the Papez's circuit are also associated with memory storage (34). Right-hemisphere stroke involving the parietal lobe in humans produces moderate impairment of memory (72). This indicates that the memory is stored widely in the brain. According to the semblance hypothesis, areas of convergence of sensory inputs occurring at different orders of neurons are potential sites where functional LINKs can form during learning and get re-activated during memory retrieval. Typical examples of sites where multiple sensory inputs reach are hippocampi and amygdale. Removing these areas induce severe memory defects for different types of memories. The immediate effects are anterograde memory problems. In addition, time-dependent loss of retrograde memories also occurs.

IV.7 Altered sensory perception

Normally, islets of LINKed postsynapses remain separated from each other (Fig.5). In disease conditions, abnormal LINKs may be formed between the unrelated islets of LINKed postsynapses. The same mechanisms of cue-induced functional semblance for memory may now induce the retrieval of memories for unassociated items causing hallucinations.

Dopamine is known to be associated with the promotion of learning associated with motivation (70, 160). It is possible that dopamine that facilitates learning through the formation of functional LINKs. From this it is reasonable to argue that dopamine antagonists that are used in the treatment of schizophrenia may block the formation mis-LINKs between the postsynapses that represent unassociated items and reduce the symptoms of the disease. The finding that some of the dopamine antagonists cause memory defects in normal individuals (93) also supports these arguments.

IV.8 Electroconvulsive stimulation and functional LINKs

Electroconvulsive stimulation/therapy (ECS/ECT) procedure used in some psychiatric disorders leads to retrograde amnesia (107). Induction of massive synchronized firing can induce the following changes. a) Induce new functional LINKs between many non-specific postsynapses that are closely placed. b) Destroy many existing functional LINKs including the mis-LINKs in the schizophrenia patients. Following ECS, a specific cue will induce many non-specific semblances leading to defects in retrograde memory retrieval. The mis-LINKs between already-formed re-LINKable functional LINKs can also contribute to anterograde amnesia.

It is possible that the abnormal mis-LINKs between the islets of functional LINKs may occur in schizophrenia patients and may lead to perception of unassociated sensory stimuli leading to hallucinations (see section IV.1). These abnormal LINKs are destroyed by ECS along with the destruction of normal functional LINKs. Therefore, ECS can induce relief of symptoms of hallucination along with defects in memories.

IV.9 Other conditions

Chronic sensory disorders of unknown aetiology, for example, tinnitus and chronic pain, may occur as a result of synaptic hallucinations of sensations in the absence of specific stimuli possibly due to the formation of misconnections at the LINKable postsynapses.

V. Hypothesis provides theoretical requirements for a memory system

The articles by Rubin et al (125) and Abbott (1) are used as preludes to examine the theoretical requirements for any system with efficient memory storage capabilities. The theoretical requirements explained by the investigators including a) provision for unlimited life-times b) absence of overwriting of old memories with new ones and c) absence of decay of the memory trace by any modifications of the basic units by new learning should hold true for any alternate hypothesis for memory storage.

It was reported that in order to explain cognitive functions of our brain, we need to build models that can provide provisions for the following three functions a) instant access to very large memory stores b) ability to generate hypotheses c) interaction between internally generated hypotheses and external evidence that allows sensory data to veto or support internal constructs extremely efficiently (1). Here, semblance hypothesis is examined to test whether it has the capabilities to provide the basic framework to explain the above features. In addition, some of the observations made by the authors of different research articles are examined based on the present hypothesis.

V.1 Memory retrieval at physiological time-scales

Functional LINKs are viewed as activity and oxygenation-state dependent transient LINKs between the postsynapses. The cue specificity determine the spread of activity reaching specific set of synapses where oxygen release induce re-activation of the functional LINKs resulting in semblance formation and concurrent spread of EPSPs to the downstream neuronal soma.

As new learning takes place, postsynapses at different neuronal levels are functionally LINKed to each other. Related learning will increase the size of the islets of LINKed postsynapses. Unrelated learning using a new cue and a new learned item is likely to produce more new sets of functionally LINKed postsynapses in addition to reactivating the already existing functional LINKs. During retrieval by a related cue using any of the postsynapses on a functionally LINKed islet, there will be concurrent EPSP-spread and formation of semblances. The latter may contribute to the neuronal activity in the downstream neuron, possibly generating a partial neuronal network activity. This additional neuronal network activity will be a new expanded one having common features with the originally learned item.

Due to changes in the functional LINKs resulting from synapse formation, elimination, neurogenesis and neuronal deaths, semblances elicited by a given cue keep changing and can lead to gradual loss of memory unless reinforced by repetition of same learning or related learning events or by maintaining the functional LINKs by unrelated learning. Even though activation of a specific

51

postsynaptic membrane was used for the derivation of the semblance hypothesis, degeneracy of the signature/code/activation pattern provides a mechanism to elicit specific semblances (section III.5). This is due to the fact that the spread of EPSP in a functionally LINKed islet of postsynapses by activating any one of the postsynapses can possibly elicit semblance of activity from the presynaptic terminals synapsing to all of them.

Based on the present hypothesis, the time required for retrieval does not depend on transcription, translation or post-translational modification of any particular protein molecule at the time of retrieval. Instead, retrieval of memory functions by using existing functionally LINKed postsynapses. The established functional LINKs will be ready to function instantaneously and explain the physiological time-scales observed during memory retrieval.

V.2 Provision for unlimited life-times

One of the requirements that need to be satisfied by a system with long memory lifetimes is unlimited lifetimes of stored memories (125). Functional LINKs that form between postsynapses are viewed as the fundamental units of the semblance hypothesis. Each postsynapse in an "islet of LINKed postsynapses" is likely to get activated during many events of related or unrelated learning or memory retrieval. This keeps the LINKs functionally active throughout life. Therefore, whenever a specific cue is used to recall a memory, these functional LINKs can be used to evoke semblance for specific memory with unlimited life-times. It also correlates with the transferability of the LINKed postsynapses in different learning and retrieval processes (section III.5). If one postsynapse is LINKed to an islet of LINKed postsynapses in a new learning event, it may lose its ability to stay LINKed unless the newly LINKed postsynapse is used continually to keep the newly made functional LINK in a LINKable state.

V.3 Absence of overwriting of old memories with new ones

Another requirement that needs to be satisfied by a system with long memory lifetimes is absence of overwriting of old memories with new ones (125). The overwriting of old memories happens if we have a system that requires changing an existing structure to give way to a new structure that is formed by additional learning. Based on the present hypothesis, there is an expanding islet of functional LINKs between the postsynapses that do not face this difficulty. Instead of overwriting, new memories can in fact use the existing functional LINKs between the postsynapses through transferability (section III.5) (also explained as degeneracy in section III.6). New memories can therefore be easily registered if a large number of pre-made functional LINKs exist from the previous learning events.

In a system with a limited number of postsynapses that can be LINKed, the number of items that can be learned may be limited once the combinations of postsynapses that can be used to determine the specific semblances for each item to be learned are used up. However, with the human brain's many orders of neurons, very large numbers of synapses, and permutations of semblances for the net functional semblance that results from synaptic delay, very large number of semblances for memories can be created without the need for overwriting old memories.

V.4 Resistance to changes in stored memory by new learning

Another major requirement for system with long memory lifetimes is resistance to changes in stored memory by new learning (125). According to the semblance hypothesis, new learning uses many existing functional LINKs by the property of transferability (section III.5)/degeneracy (section III.6). In addition, associative learning of new components leads to the expansion of many islets of existing functional LINKs. During retrieval, a specific subset of functionally LINKed postsynapses is activated. Therefore, based on the present hypothesis, decay of the memory trace by any modifications of the basic units by new learning is not an issue; rather, the activation of a set of specific postsynapses, some of which are interchangeably used by different cues in different memory retrieval events, is a feature by which net semblances from different synapses can contribute to different memories.

The functional LINKs formed by a specific event of learning can be maintained by using those LINKs either by learning or retrieval events by either related/unrelated learning or retrieval events that use them. Therefore, a cue appearing after many years will be able to induce specific net semblance for memory if the functional LINKs induced at the time of its learning has been maintained by related or unrelated learning events. By extension, it can be argued that when a less specific cue is present, the specificity of the item retrieved may be reduced (in part because more than one item is retrieved) in a system that has learned a large amount of information.

V.5 Sparseness without reduction in information storage

In order to maintain specificity, another requirement that need to be satisfied by a system with long memory lifetimes is sparseness without reduction in information storage (125). Sparseness in memory representation has been shown by theoretical studies to increase memory lifetimes (6, 144, 147, 163). Sparseness aids in retaining the specificities of the stored memories by preventing any interference between them (125). However, reduced amount of information storage by each memory is viewed as a drawback of sparseness (125). Based on the present hypothesis, there is a possible alternate solution. While probing with the cue for retrieval of memory, EPSP spreads through the functional LINKs leading to the activation of postsynaptic membranes.

Two types of activation were suggested by the semblance hypothesis. 1) A postsynaptic membrane change that is reminiscent of the arrival of the action potential at the corresponding presynaptic membrane (section II.6). 2) EPSP spreads to the postsynaptic membranes through the functional LINKs without activation of their corresponding presynaptic membranes (section II.4). Both these changes are capable of producing synaptic semblance. The latter can contribute to the generation of action potential in the postsynaptic neuron provided there are sufficient spatial and temporal summations of similar EPSPs. The activated neurons can contribute to the network semblance. Both the changes at the postsynapses marked above as numbers 1) and 2) without leading to an action potential (due to inadequate summation) will only activate isolated postsynaptic membranes, resulting in only synaptic semblance. It is the cue characteristics that decide the identity of the specific set of postsynapses where semblances occur. This specific set of postsynapses (leading to synaptic semblance) and the specific combinations of all the activated postsynapses (that induce network activity and network semblance) provide an equivalent effect of sparseness as well as the specificity required for specific memory retrieval.

V.6 Life-times of memories

Unlimited life-time is one of the requirements for any mechanism that supports memory storage functions (125). An explanation of this may be better done in the following context. It was noted that in the cortical areas like the infero-temporal cortex, memory lifetimes are presumably longer than in the medial temporal lobe and neural representations are less sparse (125). Infero-temporal cortex is crucial for visual object recognition and contains the final neuronal orders of the ventral cortical visual system. Some of the postsynapses within the islets of functionally LINKed postsynapses at the infero-temporal cortex will be shared by many sensory stimuli that can activate those sensory receptors causing their activation. Due to the degeneracy property (see section III.6), the life-times of memories will be long. Compared to infero-temporal cortex, the semblances formed at the postsynapses of the medial temporal cortex is not very stable over time. This is due to the changes in the connections brought about by new neurons formed in the hippocampus.

V.7 Instant access to very large memory stores

Instant access to very large memory stores is one of the requirements of an efficient cognitive system (1). Based on the present hypothesis, the net semblance resulting from the potentially long-lasting transient functional LINKs between the postsynapses can provide the mechanism for large amounts of associative memory storage and retrieval. Based on the characteristic features of the cue, different combinations of the postsynaptic membranes have the potential to get activated through the functional LINKs. When semblances for the sensory inputs from each one of these postsynapses as well as the network semblances are computed, the identity of the sensory stimuli that is memorized can be obtained. Therefore, semblance-based memory retrieval is instantaneous and takes place efficiently from a very large number of memory stores. Any cue (internal or external) can have instant access to very large memory stores provided specific semblance can be induced.

V.8 The ability to generate hypotheses

A system with efficient cognitive abilities should also be efficient in generating hypothesis (1). Based on the present hypothesis, a system can generate a hypothesis in the following instances. Let us assume that we are going to train an experienced nervous system, meaning that the nervous system has already been exposed to large number of diverse associative learning in its life. Based on the present hypothesis, this well-experienced nervous system can have many functional LINKs between the postsynaptic membranes at different neuronal orders. If the nervous system is exposed to a cue that was used in previous learning sessions, then the semblance of learned sensory input may easily be formed, leading to memory retrieval.

Let us now expose this nervous system to a completely novel unlearned item N instead of a cue which is part of an already learned item. Based on the present hypothesis, sensory stimuli from this novel item N will evoke activation of the postsynaptic membranes of many synapses, without the activation of their corresponding presynaptic membranes (which is the basis of the semblance hypothesis), leading to semblance for some sensory stimuli. These semblances are possible through the functional LINKs that were already established between the postsynaptic membranes during the prior learning events. Please note that many established functional and structural LINKs between the postsynaptic membranes are transferable due to the property of degeneracy (see sections III.5, III.6) during the retrieval process. The combination of the sets of postsynapses that are activated during the retrieval depends on the cue characteristics and will determine the features of the memorized item.

Let us imagine that the novel item N induces semblance for three items X, Y, Z above a certain threshold value resulting in their memory. Here, let X and Y represent items that were learned in the past. Let Z represent an unlearned item. Simultaneous semblances for X, Y and Z in the presence of N allow the nervous system to detect interrelations between these four items (even though the nervous system will require detailed experiments to explicitly confirm the relationship). In conditions where the brain/animal is appropriately trained to express those semblances that occur during exposure to a novel unlearned item, the system will be able to propose a hypothesis for an association between X, Y, Z and N which is a requirement for a system that can store memories (1).

In the previous example, semblance for Z in the presence of the novel item N provides the nervous system with semblance of a novel sensory input related to N. The nervous system may take note of it if the animal gains some advantage from it; otherwise, it gets ignored. The semblances of unlearned items when exposed to a learned cue/cues or the semblance of a learned item when exposed to an unlearned item/s may provide the means for evolutionary advantage for the nervous system of a species. It appears that the number of prior learning events, exposure to novel cues (that are not part of what was learned in the past) and attention to the semblances occurring from such exposures are key factors in hypothesis development.

Hypothesis building is part of our daily life. For example, we have pre-existing functional LINKs that calculates the mathematical operation (9 - 8) = 1. However, when exposed to a new operation of 1079-1078, we get the answer 1. We may have never done this specific mathematical operation in our life. However, we already have made enough hypotheses in our lives that whenever we minus 8 from 9 we were getting the answer 1 provided other digits are the same and have verified by real life situations to find that our results are correct. Even though we normally don't call it as a hypothesis, our interpretation that (1079 - 1078) = 1 is taken as a hypothesis for explaining semblance hypothesis.

Right hemisphere stroke involving the parietal lobe in humans produce a condition called anosognosia where the patients lack capacity to make the necessary observations and inferences to diagnose the paralysis (72). This may provide some information that semblances from the right parietal cortex have specific role on the ability for hypothesis formation, an essential feature of a system that has memory capabilities (1).

V.9 Interaction between internally generated hypotheses and external evidence

From the last section, it can be seen that the internally generated hypothesis that X, Y, Z and N are interrelated will get challenged by the availability of sensory data to veto or support it another requirement for a system with cognitive abilities (1). A typical example is how our sensory system perceives the apparent movement of the Sun around the Earth. Our nervous systems clearly sense the movement of Sun during the sunrise and sunset in relation to the stable objects in our visual field. Based on the sensory inputs of the appearance of the Sun in the east and disappearance in the west, we may hypothesize that Sun is rotating round the Earth thus vetoing the statement that it is the Earth that is rotating around the Sun. However, if explained it as an illusion, similar to the illusions in our daily lives (like the apparent movement of the trees while travelling in a car) in the context of scientific evidences that it is the Earth that is moving around the Sun, our nervous system will accept the latter.

V.10 First-time retrieval of memories after long interval of time after learning

Sometimes memories can be retrieved after many years even without retrieving them in between. How can this be explained? During learning, functional LINKs form between the postsynapses (note that the functional LINKs are transient, activity and oxygenation-state dependent). As related or unrelated learning takes place over many years, islets of functional LINKs are formed and get expanded (Fig.5). Each postsynapse in an "islet of LINKed postsynapses" is likely to get activated during many events of related or unrelated learning or memory retrieval. This is possible through the hypothesized spread of EPSP through the functionally LINKed postsynapses.

Let us now consider an important point. Let us assume that a specific learning event had taken place twenty years ago in our nervous system. We assume that one day after learning, a cue stimulus can activate a specific set (n) of postsynapses of the learned item (through the functional LINKs) to evoke semblance leading to memory. Let us also assume that continued learning in the following years had caused activation of those (n) postsynapses (few at a time during isolated events of different learning and memory retrieval) through the same functional LINKs that were activated during the initial learning (by degeneracy property as explained in section III.6).

As long as sufficient number of LINKs from other postsynapses to the (n) postsynapses under question is maintained (by different event of learning and memory retrieval), we are in a position to activate them using an appropriate cue that was used during the initial learning that took place twenty years ago. Therefore, whenever the specific cue is used to recall a memory, the specific set of postsynapses can be activated to evoke the semblance for the specific memory. This feature can provide the ability to form memories without saturation and with unlimited life-times. It also correlates with the transferability of the functional properties of the LINKed postsynapses in different learning and retrieval events. The above explained retrieval property due to the transferability property of the functional LINKs will be more efficient for very specific learning events.

V.11 LTP in terms of semblance hypothesis

The semblance hypothesis was derived to explain plausible synaptic changes occurring during learning suitable for evoking virtual sensation of a sensory stimulus during memory retrieval. One general argument is that any new hypothesis of memory should be able to explain the relationship between memory and LTP. A plausible reasoning for the relationship between memory and LTP through the semblance hypothesis is done by explaining the following experimental findings. It has been shown that one-trial inhibitory avoidance learning in rats produced the same changes in hippocampal glutamate receptors as the induction of LTP with high-frequency stimulation (162). This study showed that learning-induced synaptic potentiation occludes high-frequency stimulation-induced LTP. Based on the present hypothesis, these findings can be explained as follows.

a. Learning first followed by LTP induction

According to the semblance hypothesis, prior learning events in a caged environment would have already made many islets of LINKed postsynapses (dendritic spines) in the hippocampi of the rats as explained in figure 5. Since associative learning opportunities are finite during caged life, we can expect a slow expansion (by LINKing more postsynapses with additional related learning events) of discrete islets of LINKed postsynapses as the rats grow up. When rats undergo avoidance learning (a novel instance of associative learning), we can expect the formation of functional LINKs between two or more islets of functional LINKs that are already present in the nervous system. Even though this is particularly important in this experimental context, it will also hold true in any novel associative learning.

In experiments using inhibitory avoidance testing (162), not all the recording electrodes recorded an increase in field EPSP (fEPSP) slope, indicating that ionic changes at the locations of the tips of these electrodes (CA1 dendritic tree) required to produce an increase in fEPSP slope did not take place. However, among those electrodes that recorded an increase in fEPSP slope after inhibitory avoidance learning, a sufficient number of Shaffer-CA1 synapses were potentiated. Let I and II stand for two islets of functionally LINKed postsynapses that were already present in the animal before the avoidance learning session (Fig.19). During learning, it is likely that LINKs were formed between the islets of LINKed postsynapses I and II. This will generate a sudden increase in the size of an islet of LINKed postsynapses to nearly two-fold, forming a mega-islet of LINKed postsynapses (Fig.19)

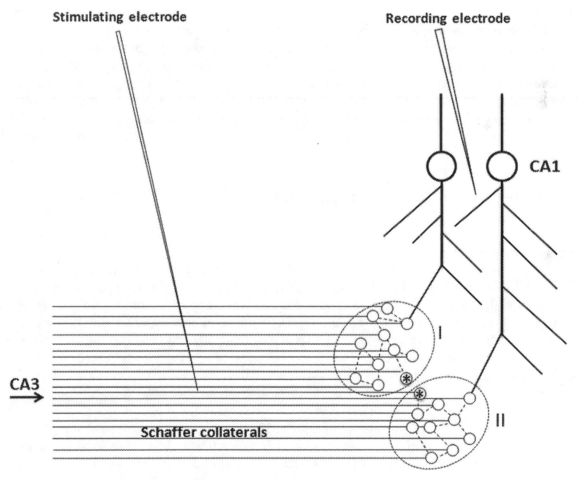

Figure19. Illustration explaining the basis of long term potentiation (LTP) based on the present hypothesis.

Shaffer collateral from the CA3 neurons synapse to the dendritic spines (postsynapses) of the CA1 neurons. Many of these postsynapses are functionally LINKed to form islets in an animal (see figure 5 for details of the islets of functional LINKs). Here two such islets I and II (large circles) are shown. One of the postsynapses from each of the islets I and II is shown to continue towards the soma of the CA1 neurons. Activation of any one of the postsynapse within an islet will result in EPSP spread towards the somas of the CA1 neuron. The islets are formed between postsynapses that are concurrently activated during previous associative learning.

During an associative learning of a novel item or during induction of LTP (note the position of the stimulating electrode is at the Schaffer collaterals), a new functional LINK may form between the postsynapses (marked asterisks) of islets I and II. This can lead to the formation of a mega-islet combining the two islets. This can contribute to the LTP recorded from the recording electrode as explained in the text.

Activation of a postsynapse of this mega-islet of LINKed postsynapses can cause spread of EPSP between its postsynapses. Since a subset of postsynapses in the mega-islet already LINKed to one of the dendritic spines (postsynaptic membranes) on the dendritic tree of one CA1 neuron, multiple EPSPs from this subset will reach the main dendrite of a CA1 neuron simultaneously. This results in a summated EPSP at this dendritic location sufficient to produce a corresponding increase in current sink in the extracellular matrix. Immediately following the associative learning event, a proportion of sensory inputs reaching the animal for a long duration of time is likely to activate the postsynapses of this mega-islet, leading to prolonged activation of the main dendrites of the above CA1 neuron (until the CA1 neuron begins homeostatic mechanisms to reduce this prolonged and increased EPSP generation). The extracellular signal recorded from the apical dendrites of a population of pyramidal neurons in the stratum radiatum of the CA1 region in response to Schaffer collateral stimulation, namely the field EPSP, will now show an increase in amplitude and contribute to an increase in fEPSP slope showing LTP. This learning-induced LTP occludes further LTP induction since the baseline increases due to the learning-induced LTP.

b. LTP induction first followed by learning

The occlusion process explained in the study (162) can be considered a bidirectional process, meaning that the induction of LTP in a sufficient number of synapses that are involved in inhibitory avoidance learning will prevent consequent avoidance learning. It is likely that hundreds of axons of the CA3 neurons in the Schaffer collateral pathway are activated by high-frequency stimulation (LTP induction), activating the postsynapses (dendritic spines) of a CA1 neuron. During this process, many postsynapses can get functionally LINKed due to the simultaneous activation of closely placed postsynapses by high-frequency stimulation (assuming that sufficient oxygenation state is present during this process). Some of these LINKs will occur between the islets of already LINKed postsynapses, leading to the generation of mega-islets. Following this, the activation of one or more postsynapses by a regular stimulus (not high frequency) can lead to the spread of EPSP between the postsynapses within the mega-islet. Since one or a subset of postsynapses in the mega-islet originates from the dendritic tree of a single CA1 neuron, multiple EPSPs from these postsynapses travel down the dendritic tree of a CA1 neuron. This results in an increase in the EPSP at these dendritic locations, leading to LTP. This artificially-induced LTP can occlude further learning-induced LTP.

If we can artificially induce LTP in a sufficient number of fibers that are critical for the learning, then the animal may not become successful in associative learning using those synapses following the LTP induction. When we say that the animal cannot learn, we mean that the animal cannot retrieve the memories; i. e., when a cue stimulus tries to retrieve a memory using these synapses, the induced EPSP spreads across all those postsynapses that are LINKed by the LTP induction. The retrieval using a specific cue now induces synaptic semblances at all those LINKed postsynapses in the mega-islet, some of which were non-specifically LINKed during the LTP induction. Activation of those non-specific postsynapses will lead to the activation of non-specific neurons, leading to the induction of non-specific network semblances that are not related to the learned item. In other words, the expected specificity of semblance for the learned item gets diluted by the large amount of non-specific semblances, preventing specific memory retrieval.

Recent work has shown that short term potentiation (STP) is a mechanism for memory (31). According to the semblance hypothesis, different types of memories have the same basic units of operation through the functional LINK formation during learning and their reactivation during memory retrieval. This may explain the relationship between the findings of STP and memory.

VI Additional Features

VI.1 Nature of the functional LINK

Using semblance hypothesis, almost all the physiological and many pathological conditions relating to memory are explained. The next step of inquiry needs to be directed towards understanding the nature of the basic units responsible for semblance, namely the LINKs.

I. *Functional LINKs:* From the previously published results from various laboratories, the possible nature of the functional LINK is examined. The main features are the following.

A. Activators of the functional LINKs

a. Oxygen is an important factor involved in inducing the oxygenation-state dependent functional LINK formation. fMRI signals indicate oxygen release from the hemoglobin. Since the peak of these signals are found 4 to 5 seconds after the neuronal firing (98), there are two possibilities. Oxygen is used either to replenish the dissolved oxygen used to oxygenate the molecules participating in the functional LINK formation or reactivation or to replenish the ATP molecules, used for functional LINK formation or re-activation, through oxidative phosphorylation for converting the reducing equivalents $NADH_2$ and $FADH_2$.

b. Glucose will be required to provide energy for all the active processes involved during the functional LINK formation or re-activation. While glucose can definitely act as a source of energy, it is not known whether glucose is directly involved in the functional LINK formation or reactivation.

c. Dopamine is known to facilitate motivation-induced learning (70, 165). It is known that the dopamine receptor expression is related with oxygen saturation in the blood (17). A direct relationship with hyperoxia and change in expression of D_2 dopamine receptors was reported earlier (17). It is not known whether a direct relationship exists that can explain the expression of dopamine receptors at locations of increased physiological oxygen during learning. It is possible that the dopamine receptor agonists activate and antagonists block the formation of the functional LINKs.

d. Amphetamine is known to act by increasing the levels of dopamine and nor-epinephrine (65). Their direct or indirect role in the functional LINK formation will need further examination.

B. Blockers of the functional LINKs

a. Glycine receptor, a ligand-gated chloride channel, may inhibit the formation of the functional LINKs. This may be inferred from the fact that strychnine, a blocker of the glycine receptor (118),facilitate learning by affecting some neurobiological processes underlying the memory storage (88).

b. GABA-activated chloride channels may inhibit functional LINK formation and reactivation since those channels are enhanced by topiramate, an antiepileptic medication that causes cognitive side effects including defects in short-term memory.

c. Electrical instability induced by electro-convulsive therapy (29) is likely to block the functional LINKs. It was reported that rats suffered loss of memory of fear responses when they received electroconvulsive shock, 24 hours after the fear-conditioning trial, which is preceded by a brief presentation of the conditioned stimulus (90). This memory loss was seen when ECT was given any time within 24 hours after conditioning, indicating the effect of electricity on some unknown factors.

d. Anesthetics may act by blocking the functional LINKs.

It may be noted that the above nature of the functional LINKs does not necessarily rule out other potential mechanisms of memory storage as discussed in section II.6. It was discussed earlier that any mechanism that can bring any type of changes that is reminiscent of the changes indicating the arrival of an action potential at the presynaptic terminal can contribute to synaptic semblance (section II.4).

II. *Structural LINKs:* As explained in section II.8.3, structural LINKs can either be formed from using genetic information or acquired during life by associative stimuli. These structural LINKs are viewed as resulting from fusion between the adjacently placed postsynaptic membranes (Fig.20).

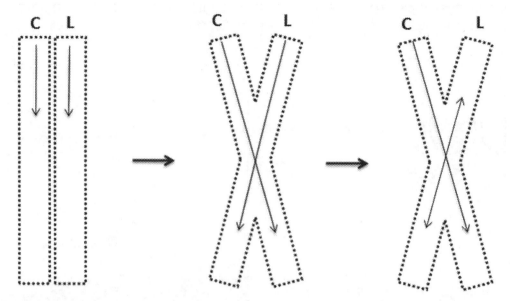

Figure 20. Schematic representation showing two adjacently placed cell membranes belonging to two different postsynapses between which functional LINK forms allowing spread of EPSP. Here, transient membrane fusion is seen as a possibility. More than one location where transient membrane fusion may take place between two functionally inter-LINKed postsynapses.

VI.2 Lateral spread of EPSPs

Evidence for electrical coupling between the pyramidal neurons (27) proposed for generating or modulating neuronal oscillations is not yet available. However, hemodynamic signals were shown to correlate tightly with synchronized gamma oscillations (104). Based on the present hypothesis, these gamma oscillations can activate many neurons simultaneously and induce functional LINKs. The role of functional LINKs generating neuronal oscillations and the neuronal oscillations inducing functional LINKs is given in section III.10.

Summation of laterally-spreading EPSPs (through the function LINKs) arriving at the dendritic tree of a neuron can induce action potentials at the soma of the neurons located laterally. These EPSPs reaching the soma is taking place in addition to those generated from normal synaptic activations. Since the EPSP-spread through the functional LINKs takes place laterally, this provides more lateral spread of activity. This is graphically demonstrated in figure 21). Hippocampus receives sensory stimuli from almost all the sensory systems in a convergent fashion making it a location where increasing number of functional LINK occurs where lateral spread of EPSPs between the postsynapses occur. These may be contributing to different neuronal rhythms within the hippocampus.

During the development of the cortex, all the cortical neuronal layers originate at the lamina I. Later, the somata move towards their final positions by anchoring their longest end of the dendritic tree to the level of the lamina I. Thus, all the neurons in different laminae have their dendritic trees extended to the lamina I. This provides sufficient spatial proximity between their postsynapses (dendritic spines) for functional LINK formation.

Note that due to the effect of lateral spread of activity through the functional LINKs, the waveforms can be recorded close to the surface of the brain and may contribute to the waveforms recorded by surface electroencephalogram (EEG). Future studies will facilitate further understanding of the contribution of the lateral spread of EPSP through the functional LINKs.

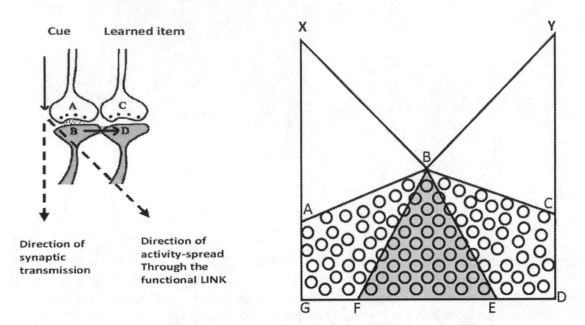

Figure 21.Schematic representation of the effect of lateral spread of EPSPs through the functional LINKs and the resulting lateral spread of neuronal activity.

Left panel: During memory retrieval by the cue stimulus, spread of activity takes two directions. (These are marked by dashed (broken) arrows). a) Direction due to the normal synaptic transmission, which is often unidirectional with some possible spread to the sides due to axonal branching (not shown in the diagram). b) Lateral spread of activity through the reactivated functional LINKs.

Right panel: Simultaneous activation of the cue and the learned item (from the vertices X and Y) results in generation of many functional LINKs between the postsynapses. Triangle ΔBEF represents the area of neuronal activation resulting from regular synaptic transmission. With the added lateral spread of EPSPs, more neurons on the lateral sides of the ΔBEF are activated. This is represented by the activation of neurons in the pentagon ABCDG.

VI.3 Equilibrium state of the semblance

Many possible consequences remain to be explored in a system that exhibits semblance. How many orders of neurons are involved in memory storage and retrieval? What determine this number? At what time the system attains states of equilibrium? How does the state of equilibrium influence the usage of the system for further learning? For example, let us assume that a cue evokes memories of a previously learned item and is followed by re-exposure to the learned item. Does the system reorganize itself? If sufficient memories already exist in the system, will re-exposure induce any new functional LINKs even if the activity continues to reach the higher neuronal orders? Computational studies may provide answers to these questions.

VI.4 Semblance – Role of inputs and outputs

The convergence of different sensory input pathways result in the formation of the functional LINKs. The action potential generation of a given neuron depends on how much input it receive from the neurons of the preceding neuronal order. Based on the present hypothesis, the EPSP generated at the postsynapses through the functional LINKs contribute to the action potential generation (in addition to concurrent semblance formation). If the spatial and temporal summated EPSPs are at sub-threshold levels for generating an action potential, then there won't be any action potential generation or subsequent activity spread to the next order of neurons. In this situation, the EPSPs spread through the functional LINKs at the postsynapses will only be able to generate synaptic semblance and not network semblance (Fig.22)

In another scenario, where if the summated EPSPs are much higher than the threshold for generating an action potential, it will there will be synaptic semblances at those postsynapses where activity reach through the functional LINKs. In addition, there will be network semblance due to the activity spread to higher orders of neurons by the action potential generated. In order to generate more network semblance, the functional LINKs should be formed between the postsynapses that belong to different neurons. This can become a possibility when dendritc trees of neurons converge. The curved structural orientation of neurons in the hippocampus and the cortex facilitates this possibility.

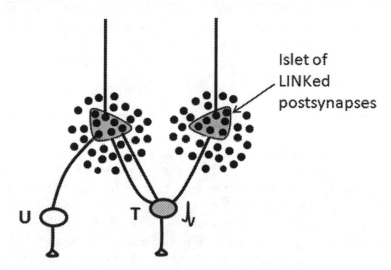

*Figure 22.The extent of the contribution of the functional LINKs between the dendritic spines (postsynapses) of a neuron determines their activity which in turn determines the generation of network semblance. In the figure the neuron **U** is not generating action potential since it is not receiving sufficient summated EPSPs. Only synaptic semblance taking place at the postsynapses where EPSP spread occurs within the islet can be contributory towards memory retrieval.*

*In contrast, the neuron **T** is firing an action potential since it receives sufficient summated EPSP possibly through more dendritic spines (postsynapses) that results in more summated EPSPs to its axon hillock. This can lead to activity in a network of neurons downstream from the neuron **T** generating network semblance contributing toward memory retrieval.*

VI.5 Viewing memory as a virtual sensation – A critical feature of the hypothesis

The new reductionistic approach used in the present hypothesis was possible only by viewing memory as a virtual sensation of a sensory stimulus. Formation of the virtual sensation during memory retrieval cannot be demonstrated by simple experiments. This is particularly important since memory is a property of the internal state of the nervous system. Since behavioural motor activities are being assessed as measures of memory retrieval during animal experiments, it will be useful to understand a) nature of the virtual sensation b) mechanism that leads to motor activities responsible for behavioural manifestation.

The nature of the internal state that provides the virtual sensation of a sensory stimulus in the latter's absence, which is proposed as a multi-dimensional semblance (Section II.4, stage 2; Figs. 9,10,11) by the semblance hypothesis, may be demonstrated by computational methods. Incorporating additional computational segments may provide the experimenter alternate methods to understand the internal state of perception of sensations (see section IX). The major question is "How does the behavioural manifestation occur as a result of the memory retrieval?"

The immediate behavioural responses can be explained based on the present hypothesis. This can be solved by examining the presence of the effects of the predicted partial neural network activation on motor outputs (Figure 7) in both computational models and experimental animals. We need to reproduce the effect of partial network using novel methods that will allow us to conceive the occurrence of memory within the internal state of the nervous system. Experiments by computational methods, nanotechnology and by indirect evidences in biological systems may provide advancement in the examination of semblance hypothesis.

VI.6 What does firing of a neuron during retrieval of memories mean?

We anticipate the firing of neurons in the higher orders along the pathway of the cue stimulus, provided they receive sufficient spatial and/or temporal summations of EPSPs. Do neurons that are not synaptically connected get fired? What if neurons that are not synaptically connected with the cue stimulus get fired? Both experimental (43, 49, 149) and computational (61, 70) studies have shown repeated firing of neurons during memory retrievals. What are these neurons? How do they represent memory? In a large nervous system with nearly 10^{10} neurons, it is very difficult to predetermine which neurons will fire during specific memory retrieval. Experiments were only able to predict that certain neurons that fired during retrieval will continue to get fired during repetition of retrievals.

The explanation for firing of these neurons can only be solved by answering the question "What does the firing of a neuron mean to retrieval of memory?" Based on the present hypothesis, both synaptic and network semblances occurring through the functional LINKs is responsible for memory. Concurrent with the induction of semblance, activation of the functional LINKs that transfer EPSPs to the postsynapses belonging to the learned item can induce action potentials provided sufficient EPSPs reach the neuron. This also initiates activation of a network that belongs to/represents the learned item, inducing network semblance (see figure 7). Based on the present hypothesis, firing of a neuron by a cue stimulus occurring only after an associative learning event indicates that some of the EPSPs that helped to fire that neuron was reached at the axon hillock through a functional LINK that was formed during learning.

In one study using a mixture of odorant cues at different concentrations, the neuronal firing in the orbito-frontal cortex was measured as a function of decision-making strategies (61). Let us assume that there is a set of neurons (X) that are fired by the cue stimulus alone. In order to calculate the number of neurons activated as a result of learning, we need to minus the set X from the total set of neurons that are activated after learning. Some neurons fired during the correct decision making and some others fired during the wrong decision making process. These can be explained in terms of the present hypothesis. Based on the network semblance, a specific cue activates specific neurons that belong to/represent the learned item through functional LINKs as explained in figure 7. A weak cue (mixture of odours), leading to a wrong decision making, can activate some other neurons through additional functional LINKs. As the proportion of the cue mixture varies, the re-activated functional LINKs and the set of activated neurons changes. When the network semblance formed by their activity does not match with the expected semblance, it will not evoke correct memory.

VI.7 How many orders of neurons are required?

It may be assumed that the number of orders of neurons that the cue stimulus need to pass through in order to effectively produce sufficient net semblance for memory retrieval is a reasonable measure of the number of orders of neurons involved in memory storage and retrieval. This depends on the order of neurons at which convergence of sensory inputs occurs and the effective semblance formed at the LINKed postsynapses at those locations. We understand about memory retrieval of a nervous system of an animal through the motor outputs that allow communication through the spoken language or through the motor activities. Based on the present hypothesis, effect is achieved through the activation of the partial neuronal network that belongs to/represents the learned item by the cues stimulus.

a) Memory of an item: The cue stimulus enters the nervous system by many sensory inputs. It is possible that there is optimum number of neurons that can induce appropriate memories during retrieval.

b) Continuity in visual perception: How many synapses through which the sensory inputs must travel in order to continuously perceive a sensory input? This can be examined through some observations in the visual system. In old system of movie projection, the film reel was used at speeds of more than 16 frames per second for visualizing the movie as a continuous event. Individual visual frames can only be perceived when the reel is rolled at speeds less than 16 frames per second. It means that continuous perception of a visual scene needs $1/16^{th}$ seconds (62.5 milliseconds). Let us assume that the normal synaptic delay is nearly 2 milliseconds. Therefore, it is reasonable to assume that during the interval of 62.5 milliseconds, light would have travelled through nearly 30 synapses (nearly 30 neuronal orders). We can integrate the net semblances by using combination of semblances occurring at each neuronal order and permutation of semblances occurring at different orders of neurons.

VI.8 Memory locations within the brain

The classic work of Lashley (69) had shown that memory is widely distributed throughout the brain. One critical finding in the study was that the number of trials required for re-learning a maze problem after a cortical lesion was proportional to the extent of the lesion. According to the semblance hypothesis, semblance formed at the regions of convergence of sensory inputs is the basis of memory. It is likely that the above study may have done trials to form net semblances just above the threshold for memory. In other words, the crucial functional LINKs through which the cue stimulus passes through to evoke effective net semblance for memory will be reduced below the threshold after the surgery. Putting it in another way, excessive repetitions of learning might not have been carried out to induce excessive semblances that can withstand surgical removal of a part of the cortex.

In another study, visual memory was found to decline after unilateral anterior temporal lobe resection (28). From the results of the study, it can be assumed that significant number of semblances required for visual memory retrieval for spatial locations takes place mainly at the left anterior temporal lobe. However, the study also showed that there were variations among the subjects regarding the locations where memories for spatial locations take place. Even though the anatomical pathways in the human brain are almost similar among individuals of a species, resections of specific locations of the brain in different individuals produced different outcomes, indicating the possibility that either there are differences in the locations of functional LINKs formed for a specific memory or differences in the weights of contribution of semblances from particular postsynapses to the net functional semblance.

VI.9 Short-term and long-term memories

The view that short-term and long-term memories operate through different mechanisms has been challenged by different experiments (19, 25, 41, 126). According to the semblance hypothesis, the basic unit of the functioning of the working, short term and long term memories is the same. Thus, semblance hypothesis is in agreement with earlier suggestion that working memory is not as a separate system but is a part of long-term memory (18-20, 25, 41, 119, 126).

In one study, both neural and behavioral evidences were shown to prove that maintenance of working memory contributes to the long-term memory formation (119). This work showed that the early stage of working memory maintenance contributes to successful long-term memory formation, and that this effect is mediated by a network that includes the dorso-lateral prefrontal cortex and the hippocampus (119).

Based on the present hypothesis, the basic difference between different types of memories depends on the mechanisms that govern the duration of time of re-activability of the functional LINKs that were formed between the post-synapses during learning. Most of the functional LINKs that provide semblance for working memory is very transient and therefore the cue stimuli will not be able to re-activate sufficient number of them to elicit net semblance for memory retrieval after long interval of time from the original learning. There are many factors that increase the duration of re-activability of the functional LINKs. For example, motivation-induced dopamine release (75, 108, 123, 165) is a contributing factor that may possibly act by stabilizing the functional LINKs formed during learning. In addition, locations where associative memories take place and the convergence patterns of the fibers from the associatively learned items may also be important factors in deciding the strength of permanence of a functional LINK.

According to the present hypothesis, long-term memories result from the long-term maintenance of the functional LINKs formed during one learning event. This can be achieved by maintaining those functional LINKs by activating them during repetition of the same learning, or related or unrelated learning or reactivating them during events that cause memory retrieval. These will prolong the maintenance of the specific functional LINKs for longer period of time promoting long-term memory. In addition, the transfer of the locations towards the cortex, as a result of neurogenesis occurring at the hippocampus (see section III.9), may aid in achieving specificity of overlapping semblances (see figure 9) through the functional LINKs in the cortex and may aid in long-term memory.

By extension of the arguments made in the earlier sections, it can be seen that certain possible mechanisms operate that facilitates conversion of short-term memories to long-term ones. As discussed earlier, functional LINKs form during a new learning. If the functional LINK is not used for either repetition of learning or related learning or new learning, it may lose the ability to get re-LINKed.

Long-term memories can be a function of maintenance of those functional LINKs either by transferable use (degeneracy property explained in section III.6) or input non-specificity (section III.7). Once a specific cue arrives, it will lead to the activation of a specific combination and permutation of the synapses and lead to the formation of a specific semblance for a specific memory. In summary, for long-term memory of a learned event it is essential to have a) formation and activation of large number of functional LINKs that can withstand losing a majority of them b) formation/re-activation of maximum possible number of functional LINKs in the cortex that can contribute to specificity to the retrieved item through semblance.

VI.10 Forgetting

Forgetting can take place in two conditions. a) Forgetting due to non-use. This depends on the novelty and complexity of the learned item which will determine the number of new functional LINKs formed which are not reactivated by repetition of the learning or related learning or unrelated learning events b) aging and degenerative changes in the nervous system.

It was mentioned earlier (see section III.2) that the newly formed functional LINKs are unstable. Most of them get destabilized unless reactivated. In addition, increase in the number of associative learning events in a given nervous system can cause expansion of the islets of functional LINKs. Increase in the size of the islets of functional LINKs can produce increased sensitivity of memory retrieval at the cost of specificity in a nervous system with a limited number of synapses. In addition new synapse formation, synapse deletion and neurogenesis will lead to dilution of the specificity of the net semblance leading to forgetting.

VI.11 Measures to increase memory and to prevent its loss

From the semblance hypothesis, it can be seen that the following steps may increase the efficiency of memory retention in a given nervous system.

1. Optimal interval for repetition of learning that provides maximum increase in net semblance is determined by the rate of neurogenesis. This will facilitate incorporation of more hippocampal and cortical synapses which in turn increase the number of functional LINKs at which semblances can be elicited for efficient memory retrieval.

2. Increasing physical activity known to improve neurogenesis in the hippocampus (155) is a possible method to improve memory by improving the efficiency of repetition of learning.

3. It is known that pseudo-dementia is associated with depression and that neurogenesis is inhibited during clinical depression. Treating depression with antidepressants improves both neurogenesis and memory (7, 127).

4. Functional LINKs are transferable (section III.5). Therefore, related or unrelated learning can improve memory storage mechanism. The extent of this property requires further exploration.

5. Motivation that can induce release of dopamine may also contribute to the formation and stabilization of the functional LINKs. Staying motivated while learning can improve the formation and long-time maintenance of the functional LINKs.

VI.12 Plausible explanation for innate and Zombie behaviours

Based on the present hypothesis, behavioral activity is often guided by the semblances and the accompanying partial neural network activities that guide the execution of appropriate motor actions. Acute survival responses may depend on the motor responses guided by the activation of the partial network belonging to the learned item. Activities of the partial neuronal network (Fig.7) , that are activated through structural LINKs, can explain the innate behaviors of the newborns like rooting and sucking reflexes that occur in the absence of any prior learning.

Nervous systems can perform many behavioral tasks without direct conscious awareness of it (63). Based the present hypothesis, a feasible explanation can be made as follows. Sensory inputs passively reaching the nervous system will induce activation of the partial neuronal network (Fig.7) resulting in motor activities responsible for behavioral manifestations without awareness.

VII. Principles and corollaries of the hypothesis

VII.1 Principles

1. *A unit of memory, in the presence of an internal or external cue stimulus, results from the ability to induce specific postsynaptic events at the synapses of the neurons from the learned item without the requirement of action potentials reaching their presynaptic sides.*

2. *In a network of neurons receiving a continuum of sensory inputs, instantaneous activation of a specific subset of postsynapses at different orders of neurons will induce semblance of a sensory input that the specific subset of postsynapses represent.*

3. *In order to activate a specific subset of postsynapses without the requirement of activating their presynapses, it is required to have functional LINKs between the postsynapses of the cue stimulus and the item retrieved. The name "functional" is due to the fact that its transient existence is a function of activity reaching the postsynapse of the cue stimulus and the previous associative learning that induced its formation.*

4. *Since synaptic semblance at the postsynapse and network semblance from the subsets of normal networks belong to/represent the learned item induce a virtual sensation of a sensory input, physical presence of the neuronal pathways connecting the above locations with the sensory receptors are not required for memory retrieval. This is a property of a network of neurons receiving a continuum of sensory inputs.*

5. *For semblance to occur as a result of activation of a postsynapse (or similar changes described) through the functional LINKs, it is required that the synapse would have functioned normally (presynaptic activation leading to postsynaptic EPSPs) at an earlier occasion.*

6. *Newly formed functional LINKs are highly transient. Unless repetition of activation or the presence of factors that stabilizes the LINKs is available at the time of learning newly formed functional LINKs may not be able to get re-activated at a later stage.*

The principle number 2 explained above requires a continuum of sensory inputs. The background sensory inputs an animal receive and the neuronal oscillations in the hippocampus and cortex provide the continuum of activity inputs. The principle number 5 explained above needs some clarification. What is the minimal requirement for semblance to occur at a synapse? Synapses should have functioned independently before getting functionally LINKed during a learning event. This prior normal activity of a synapse is a requirement for all the types of semblances. Once this is achieved, any activation of the postsynaptic membranes without activating its presynaptic terminals will evoke semblance. Even though these are broad frameworks, detailed examination may find exceptions that are very common in biological systems.

VII.2 Corollaries

1. Activation of at least a pair of synapses is required for associative learning to occur. (This is in contrast to the strengthening of single synapses by other previous hypotheses).

2. Retrieval of memory does not occur randomly; rather it is evoked by an internal or external cue stimulus.

3. The earliest neuronal order where semblance starts to occur is where the cue and the learned item stimuli converge.

4. If inputs from two stimuli do not meet at a sufficient number of LINKable postsynaptic membranes, at their higher orders of neuronal connections, then learning between them is not possible.

5. Normally learning activities use many previously LINKed postsynapses and use them during memory retrieval. If learning is totally novel, that prevents using previously LINKed postsynapses, then even working memory will not operate efficiently. Trying to learn a new language using another new language is an example.

6. Semblances at the LINKed postsynaptic membranes at a given order of neuron may vary over time and with continued learning. Memory retrieval depends on the net strength of semblance from all the orders of neurons.

7. Firing of a neuron by a cue stimulus occurring only after an associative learning event in previous experiments (149) indicates that some of the EPSPs that helped to fire that neuron were reached at the axon hillock through the functional LINKs that were formed during that specific learning event.

8. Memory retrieval depends on the net strength of synaptic and network semblances from all the orders of neurons. The strength of different types of semblances at different orders of neurons will vary.

9. The semblance formed at the postsynapses of functional LINKs of a neuron at a specific location of the brain of two different members of an animal species depends on the number of effective previous associative learning.

10. The specific nature of the retrieved memories after a learning event varies with time due to the changes in semblances that can occur from one postsynapse of a functional LINK due to other learning events that take place during that time interval.

11. A subset of functional LINKs formed during one learning event can be reactivated during a related or unrelated learning, enabling semblances formed from them transferable.

VIII. Experimental support

VIII.1 Supporting-evidence from the studies in the lateral amygdala

The amygdala is a brain region where strong conditioned learning changes associated with survival needs are being studied. Both cortical and thalamic inputs reach the lateral amygdala (LA). This provides opportunities to carry out electrophysiological studies using the brain slices. It is known that the LA is the site of convergence of sensory inputs carrying information about conditioned and unconditioned stimuli to the amygdala (26, 71, 83, 87). The results from a study examining the cue-associated learning of reward at the thalamo-amygdala synapses (149) are used to examine the findings in the light of the semblance hypothesis.

1. Based on the results of the study, it was concluded that learning induced some changes at the thalamo-amygdalar synapses that caused the firing of additional LA neurons. In other words, after learning, additional neurons are recruited to encode reward-predictive cues as individual rats improved their reward-learning performance. The learning ability of the rats was directly proportional to the additional number of neurons recruited to fire in the presence of the cue stimulus during memory retrieval. It is not yet known how these additional neurons in the LA fire during the retrieval of memory. According to the semblance hypothesis, these additional neurons belong to/ represent the learned item. During learning, functional LINKs are formed between the postsynapses of the synapses belonging to the cue and the learned item at locations of convergence (LA in fear conditioning). During retrieval, activity from the cue pass through the LINKed postsynapses at the LA where synapses from two different sensory inputs converge. The EPSPs spreading through the functional LINKs will reach the dendritic tree of the neurons belonging to the learned item. As a result, at the regions of convergence we expect spatial and temporal summation of EPSPs. This causes the cue alone to activate additional neurons at the same neuronal order (as explained by the partial neuronal network activation in section II.4.1.20 (Fig.7)).

2. The above study (149) has shown that the miniature EPSP (mEPSP) amplitude increases after the learning. An increase in mEPSP amplitude indicates an increase in the number or function of alpha-amino-3-hydroxy-5-methyl-4-isoxazolepropionic acid receptors (AMPARs) (81). One of the possibilities

is that the increase in mEPSP amplitude could be explained as a function of the additional AMPA channel currents from the functionally LINKed postsynapses. It is possible that the postsynaptic functional LINKs formed in the LA is not highly oxygenation state-dependent in their function, probably due to the formation of (F→S→F) LINKs. Fear conditioning is a learning process associated with survival. Therefore, it is possible that (F→S→F) LINKs occur at this brain region (associated with fear) can induce near-structural changes at the functionally LINKed postsynapses leading to permanent associative learning. Similar changes may explain post-traumatic stress that lasts longer.

3. The above mentioned changes may explain some of the results observed during the electrophysiological experiments using brain slices. Oxygenation levels in the bath solution used in the experiments could have provided sufficient oxygenation levels to re-activate the functional LINKs. Alternatively, oxygen available in the bath solution could have been sufficient enough to activate the already formed functional LINKs during learning.

4. The AMPAR/NMDAR ratio is increased at the thalamo-amygdala synapses. Based on the present hypothesis, during learning, functional LINKs are formed between the postsynapses belonging to the sensory inputs from the cue and the reward. Since thalamic afferents contain sensory afferents from both the cue and the reward sensory inputs, it can be assumed that functional LINKs are formed during learning at the locations where the thalamic afferents synapse on to the dendritic spines of the pyramidal neurons of LA. When thalamic afferents were stimulated to measure the EPSCs by patch clamping the pyramidal neurons at the LA, an increase in the amplitude of the AMPA current is observed after learning. It is possible that the measurement included AMPA currents from the neighbouring synapses that were functionally LINKed during learning.

VIII.2 Results from other studies

a) In one study (61), using a mixture of odorant cues at different concentrations, the neuronal firing in the orbito-frontal cortex was measured as a function of the decision-making strategies. Some neurons fired during the correct decision-making and some others fired during the wrong decision-making process. Based on the network semblance, it is conceivable that a specific cue of sufficient strength activates specific neurons through its functional LINKs. Even though a partial cue (mixture of odours) can evoke partial semblances for the item to be memorized, the network semblance formed by the evoked neuronal activity need not be sufficient to evoke the correct memory. This leads to wrong decision making.

b) Another study (60) has shown that repeated retrieval induced through testing (and not repeated encoding during additional study) produces large positive effects on long-term retention of memory. This indicates that retrieval itself can re-activate the functional LINKs made during learning. This means that once initial learning achieves retrieval-efficiency, retrieval sessions alone can activate the partial network (see figure 7) of the already formed neuronal network belonging to the learned item through the functional LINKs.

c) In another study (22), it was shown that some locations of the brain transfer the functional units of learning for another event of learning. In other words, in situations where functional LINKs are mainly present in one order of neurons in a particular brain region in a specific learning paradigm, it is likely that some of the established functional LINKs may be shared by new related learning. Specific overlapping of the components in different learning involving the same brain region can thus contribute to an improvement in performance on an untrained task, indicating the possibility that some of the established functional LINKs can be transferable. Semblance hypothesis explains sufficient mechanisms for such transfer (see section III.5).

d) Another study (43) has shown the re-activation of single neurons of a partial network in the human hippocampus that can represent the learned item. According to the semblance hypothesis, the same cue will activate the same neuronal network that was activated by the learned item to elicit network semblance immediately after learning. Therefore, it is expected that during specific memory recall firing by the same neurons can occur.

VIII.3 Oxygenation-state and spread of chemical reaction between the dendritic spines

Studies to test the activity and oxygenation dependent functional LINKs between the postsynapses *in vivo* using learning is the ideal method to test the hypothesis. Current technology is not sufficient to carry out these experiments. Oxygen release at the location of synaptic activity occurs within 4 to 5 seconds (98). One of the reasons is that oxygen is released to replenish the oxygen that was used in oxidative phosphorylation reaction to replenish energy used in the cellular process of learning. Alternatively oxygen may be used to oxidize some of the key molecules involve in the process. Here, we carried out an experiment to examine whether oxygenation state has any structural impact at the synaptic level. In vitro experiments to test for functional LINKs between adjacent dendritic spines by altering the oxygenation status are an alternative.

A simple experiment was carried out by examining whether any oxygenation-state dependent chemical continuity is present between the dendritic spines. Golgi staining (13, 45) remains a method to study dendritic spine morphology. Chemical reactions leading to the deposition of black silver chromate progress from the cut end of the neuronal processes towards other parts, making those neurons visible among groups of unstained neurons. Normally, a strong oxidizing agent oxidizes the neuronal contents during the initial step of the protocol. This is followed by the conversion of silver nitrate to silver chromate. We asked the question of whether by inducing an oxidation state difference is it possible to extend the Golgi chemical reaction from one dendritic spine to the neighbouring ones. Since a strong oxidizing agent is used as the initial step in routine Golgi staining, one possible way to address this question was to lower the oxidation status of the tissue before the staining. A large increase in the oxidation state difference was achieved by reducing the basal oxidation state by perfusing the reducing agent ascorbic acid followed by routine Golgi staining.

Rapid Golgi staining protocol (35, 48) was modified and carried out as follows. Adult mice were sacrificed by administering an overdose of carbon dioxide. Immediately, cardiac perfusion with normal saline was performed to remove blood from the vascular system. To change the oxidation state, vascular perfusion of isotonic mixture of 0.1% ascorbic acid and 5.08% sucrose (or 8.67% sodium chloride) for 5 minutes was carried out. The brain was dissected out and transferred into a solution made from potassium dichromate (250mg), chloral hydrate (250mg), 4% formaldehyde in PBS, pH 7.4 (250µL), 50% glutaraldehyde (250µL), dimethyl sulfoxide (6µL) made up to 5mL with water in a small glass bottle with aluminum foil wrap. The bottle was kept on a shaker for 4 days.

After this, brain was washed with deionized water in a separate bottle for 5 minutes. The brain was cut into two pieces 2 mm away from the area of interest. The pieces were kept in 0.75% silver nitrate solution in deionized water for 60 to 72 hours in a fresh bottle with aluminum foil wrap on a shaker. Briefly, the brain was washed with deionized water and kept in an isotonic 5.27% sucrose solution for 2 days. Using a Vibratome, the brain was cut at 75µM thickness by immersing the brain in an isotonic 5.27% sucrose solution. Next, the sections were transferred the sections to a glass slide and serial dehydrations in 50%, 70%, and 100% ethanol series was done for 5 minutes each followed by clearing by xylene for 15 minutes. The excess of xylene was removed, mounted; cover slipped and examined using a differential interference contrast microscope.

In contrast to the normal Golgi staining patterns of dendritic spines, present experiments did not show a complete filling of these structures (Fig.23.A). Instead, the presence of a clear colorless area likely to be synaptic zones/presynaptic terminals is seen on them. Alternatively, it is possible that the dark stain is present around the dendritic spines. The adjacent dendritic spines, between which spread of silver staining reaction takes place, could belong to the same or different neurons. In the cortex, the spread of chemical reaction was limited to dendritic terminals (8 ± 5.6 (S.D); n = 113 clusters) (Fig.23.B). In the hippocampal CA3 region, the spread of chemical reaction occurring in a large number of dendritic spines (482 ± 56 (S.D); n = 106 clusters) was visible (Fig.23.C).

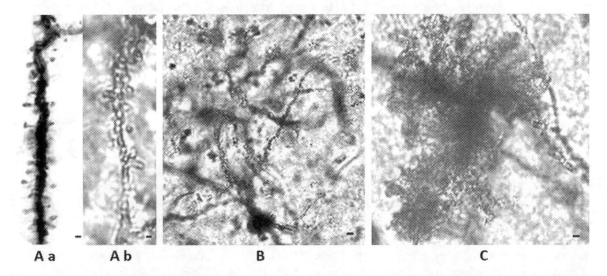

A a   A b   B   C

Figure 23.A. Dendritic spines seen in a) conventional Golgi staining and b) modified Golgi staining. Note that the spines made visible by the modified Golgi staining have a white area on/around them.

It is possible that this marks the location of the presynaptic terminal synapsing on them. Alternatively, it is possible that the dark stain is present around the dendritic spines (Scale bar = 2μm).

Figure 23.B. One cortical neuron stained by the modified Golgi staining protocol. Notice the presence of many chemically interconnected dendritic spines at the dendritic branch terminals (8 ± 5.6 (S.D); n = 113 clusters). Also note the presence of normal dendritic spines on the dendritic shafts (Scale bar = 6μm).

Figure 23.C. Large chemically-interconnected cluster of dendritic spines on the dendrite of a CA3 neuron in the hippocampus. Note that these large clusters of interconnected dendritic spines (482 ± 106 (S.D); n = 106 clusters) have more than thirty times the number of dendritic spines on a single spine neck reported on a dendritic excrescence (10, 14) (Scale bar = 6μm).

These experimental results only show that there is a possible spread of chemical reactions between the dendritic spines in an oxidation state-dependent manner. It does not provide any information whether the formation of functional LINKs between these dendritic spines is possible. These preliminary results also show that in the cortex, the size of chemically LINKed postsynapses is smaller than those at the hippocampal CA3 dendrites.

The finding of large chemically interconnected cluster of dendritic spines at the CA3 region of the hippocampus is in support of the hypothesized large islets of functional LINKs. It also support the finding of giant miniature excitatory postsynaptic currents (mEPSCs) at the hippocampal mossy fiber to the CA3 pyramidal cell synapse *in vitro* (52). Since the amplitude of the mEPSC depends on the increase in AMPA receptor function or number (81), it is likely that the large islets of functional LINKs at the large LINKed postsynapses on the dendritic spines of the CA3 neurons may be responsible for the giant mEPSCs.

VIII.4 Required experimental studies

Different supporting evidences for the hypothesis were explained in the previous chapters. The hypothesis can be directly tested by examining the premises that were used to derive it. The following studies are some of the essential ones.

1. Study the changes taking place at the junction between the postsynapses of the neurons belonging to the cue and the learned item. These include oxygenation-state dependent functional LINKs that were hypothesized to induce spread of EPSP between the postsynapses. Investigations should also include testing possible changes in the membrane structure. The size of the postsynapses is beyond the resolution of any microscopes under which patch clamp experiments can be carried out. Moreover, available size of the tip of the electrodes is far bigger than the required sizes to carry out any patch clamping on to an isolated postsynapse (imagining that it is possible). Therefore, we may not be able to prove any direct electrophysiological LINK between two postsynapses in the immediate future. For the time being, we may have to depend on corroborative evidence similar to the observation of the increased AMPA current amplitude in fear conditioning experiments carried out by Tye et al (149) (section VIII.1).

2. Searching for molecules that can sense the sequence of ionic changes in the extracellular matrix (ECM), which is proposed as a postsynaptic event reminiscent of the arrival of an action potential at its presynaptic terminal can be carried out.

3. It may also be necessary to examine possible physical properties like "inductive depolarization" that may be responsible for the functional LINKs. This possibility need to be considered as a mechanism, since it is possible that alternations in such inductive states may explain the loss of memory after electroconvulsive stimulation (107).

4. Modified Golgi staining protocol as explained in section VIII.2 has shown spread of chemical reaction possibly between the postsynapses. Electron microscopic studies of the membranes to examine the nature of the spread might provide further information.

Given the difficulties in studying the activity and oxygenation-state-dependent functional LINKs in the biological system, it appears that the present hypothesis can be tested faster by building computational models. Once successful, it may be possible to translate the knowledge to the physical systems using nano-technological methods.

IX. Computational modeling

The fact that memory is a virtual sensation of sensory inputs makes reductive approaches in biological experiments difficult to understand the nature of the retrieved memories. Computational studies, though challenging, may offer alternate ways to understand and interpret semblances that lead to memory. Simultaneous fine tuning of a very large number of variables that will be necessary for understanding the nature of semblances can be achieved by computational modeling. Here, a step wise approach that may provide answers to solve the problem is given.

1. Different sensory receptors and neuronal orders from it can be developed. Postsynapses of the synapses at the fifth to seventh neuronal orders from different sensations can be allowed to converge at the hippocampus.

2. Based on the closeness of the postsynapses and their simultaneous activation, functional LINKs are allowed to form during learning.

3. Based on the assignment of the positions of the postsynapses, we can assign values of semblances at each postsynapse.

4. A rigid model is needed to be created initially before adding the flexibility due to synapse elimination, synapse addition and hippocampal new neuron formation.

5. Given the fact that the structure of the artificial nervous system is known, make a list of all the potential functional LINKs that can be formed provided there is simultaneous activation of the postsynapses that can LINK them during various associative learning sessions.

6. Make a list of all the network semblances that can be formed.

7. Identify the synaptic semblance values that can be formed at each of the LINKable postsynapses.

8. Identify the potential network semblance values for each neuron based on the LINKable positions of their dendritic spines (postsynapses). This can provide the nature of the network semblances.

9. Learning is carried out by using a cue and an item to be learned. Expected functional LINKs that are likely to be formed between the postsynapses of

the neurons belonging to the cue and the item at different neuronal orders (where the synapses belonging to the cue and the learned item come to functionally LINKable distances) are marked.

10. Since learning in an adult nervous system depends on all the structural and functional LINKs already existing in the brain, we may need to induce several associative learning (and therefore functional LINKs) before we can expect efficient memory retrieval using a new learning test that we are planning to execute.

11. We need to standardize a large number of variables for a given nervous system in order to understand the mechanism completely. These include a) required prior associative learning and the number of functional LINKs formed from them b) nature of the theta/gamma rhythms that can provide 1) reactivation of already formed functional LINKs 2) sub-threshold activation of many neurons at higher orders 3) new neuron formation and change in semblance locations that occur during transfer of memories from the hippocampus to the cortex (see section III.9).

12. Once sufficient learning is done, introduce a specific cue for retrieving the memory. Identify all the specific synaptic and network semblances that occur at the LINKed postsynapses in the presence of the cue.

13. Plot the sensory neuron location map from each of the synaptic and network semblances. Next, integrate these sensory neuron location maps and make a sensory identity map of the item retrieved (Figs.9, 10). Extrapolate the sensory identity of the item retrieved. By comparing its characteristic features with that of the learned item, fine-tune the artificial nervous system to obtain a good match of the sensory density map. This fine-tuning needs to be carried by changing the factors given in Table 3. These factors can lead to certain level of fluctuation of the identity of the retrieved memory using a given cue over time due to addition and deletion of synapses, addition of new neurons, and formation of new functional LINKs from new learning events.

> **Table 3.** *Factors that are needed to be fine-tuned to obtain an anticipated sensory density map during memory retrieval. These factors will depend on the complexity of the nervous system, learning and the repetition of learning and previous functional LINKs present in the brain.*

1. Number of neuronal orders

2. Orders at which neuronal axons converge for potential functional LINK formation during learning

3. Number of the functional LINKs at each neuronal order

4. The extent of functional LINKs already present from previous learning

5. The extent of the partial neuronal networks

6. Weights for synaptic and network semblance

7. Smaller size of the islets of functional LINKs in the cortex and larger size of the islets in the neuronal order matching CA3 (based on the experimental findings shown in figure 23)

8. Possible permutations of the temporal activation of synapses required for action potential generation

9. Possible combinations of the synaptic activities required for action potential generation

10. Factors like neurogenesis and addition and deletion of new synapses

11. Role of inhibitory neurotransmission in the formation and re-activation of the functional LINKs

Since there are many factors that need to be fine-tuned at a given time, it will require a huge computational effort. A novice artificial nervous system (corresponding to a nervous system belonging to a child in the first few years of life) designed using computational models will have (S→F) LINKs (see section II.8.3) to maintain the basic brain functions. We need to teach the artificial nervous system by exposing it to simultaneous sensory stimuli for associative learning prior to obtaining any useful output during memory retrieval. This is primarily due to the fact that each associative learning uses many functional LINKs formed during prior associative learning. Many of the learning can utilize transferability property of the functional LINKs at different areas of the brain which is a function of the architecture of a given nervous system.

Different cue stimuli will induce the same synaptic semblance when they pass through one LINKed postsynapse to the postsynapse that belongs to the item to be retrieved. One cue stimulus activates a synapse in an islet of postsynapses and spreads through the functional LINKs to produce different synaptic semblances. Many of these activated postsynapses within an islet of functional LINKs do not belong to/represent the learned item. The synaptic semblances resulting from their activation will have only negligible contribution towards the net semblance for the memory to be retrieved.

Since the number of LINKable postsynapses is finite and the item to be memorized can be complex, learning capacity will be determined by the number of specific combinations/permutations of synaptic and network semblances. Learning of related items will require newer items for associative learning through the functional LINKs in addition to activations of previously induced functional LINKs to reach the threshold semblance for their retrieval. Newly formed neurons can bring an additional capacity for combinations or permutations of semblances at the orders of neurons above their level and can create new neuronal network semblance providing the specificity required for memory for additional items to be memorized using the same sensory system. This depends on the percentage contribution of transmission of activities through the new neurons.

Computational approaches may provide feasibility to examine the effect of multiple variables at a given time to optimize the required semblance output. Eventually we hope that the computational fine-tuning will be able to provide answers to the following questions.

1. What is the required number of the functional LINKs at each neuronal order for effective semblance?

2. What is the extent of the partial neuronal networks for effective semblance?

3. What weights are required to be given for synaptic and network semblance for effective memory?

4. At what neuronal orders should the axons converge for potential functional LINK formation during learning in a given nervous system?

5. How many orders of neurons does a sensory stimulus travel? This may in turn depend on the efficiency of a given nervous system and the net semblance that need to be made for memory retrieval. Depending of the items that need to be associatively learned for survival in a particular environment, evolutionary changes may have played a role in the development of the nervous system in different species (see section XI.5)

X. Intelligent machines

Is it wrong in assuming that machines that suitably simulate human brains have intelligence? An artificial system similar to that of the nervous system where functional LINKs can be formed between the postsynapses can be created using the principles of the present hypothesis. The elements of the machine should be able to receive background stimuli and have oscillating neuronal activities. Once learning is complete, then the cue stimulus can be used to evoke both the synaptic and network semblances. We anticipate that in a network of neurons undergoing oscillations and receiving a continuum of sensory inputs, instantaneous activation of a specific subset of postsynapses at different orders of neurons (by the cue stimulus) will induce semblance of sensory input.

We anticipate that semblances forming memory is an internal property of the nervous system. The first question here is how to test that the system has memory. We actually don't know the internal state of the animal. In real-life situations when we test memory retrieval abilities, animals show behavioral features. For example, foot withdrawal in fear-conditioning experiments. Based on these findings, we assume that that the animal has memory. If the machine shows motor outputs, by inference, will we be ready to interpret that they have memory? What is limiting is our ability to make machines that mimic human brains.

Memory retrieval experiments in animals are interpreted using animal behaviour that requires motor responses. According to the present hypothesis, a partial neuronal network (belonging to the learned item) is activated by the cue stimulus and can be responsible for downstream activation of some of the motor neurons. How to test an intelligent machine, which does not have a motor system, for memory retrieval? Here, the artificial system will need an extra segment that calculates the semblances resulting from a specific cue and provides us with the net semblance as a measurable output (additional computation can be used for this purpose).

As discussed earlier in the discussion part of the derivation of the hypothesis, for a given nervous system, all the possible semblances from individual synaptic and network semblances can be calculated initially. From this calculation, the net semblance during memory retrieval by a given cue can be estimated. This net semblance needs to be calibrated with the partial neuronal activity that can induce anticipated specific motor activities. By converting the specific semblances to measurable outputs, the system can be used to understand the feature of net semblances that are formed from a particular cue stimulus. Equivalent changes in the system for dynamic synapse addition, synapse elimination (computational studies may reveal whether these changes occur by cause or effect) and neurogenesis need to be incorporated.

The second question is how to build a system with memories that can be used by us. The best use of these intelligent machines will be their abilities to induce a tertiary semblance in response to a novel cue as explained in section II.16. The semblances produced by a machine in response to a novel cue can be tested for the accuracy. A machine that is taught to associatively learn all the knowledge in a field of study can be exposed to a novel cue for possible answers that human brains cannot normally make since the percentage of associative learning that can be re-activated in human brains are limited. The semblances formed in the intelligent machine for a novel cue can be calculated and then be verified by experiments.

It was discussed earlier that if we plan to make intelligent machines we need to introduce functional LINKs at various orders of the neurons in a temporal fashion. Once theoretical work is complete, applications of thin layer chemistry and nanotechnology may provide opportunities to build and test semblance hypothesis. Once we know the operation of semblance hypothesis in a computational model, we should be able to modify it to develop superior machines. It may be noted that human brain takes thousands of hours to mature through multitude of associative learning to reach the mature state. Therefore, if we are planning to build intelligent machines, then we will need to introduce large number of functional LINKs before expecting any reliable memory outputs.

XI. Discussion

The complete understanding of the properties of the neurons and their synaptic connections are basic requisites for understanding how associative memories are formed (113). The present work has examined memory as a virtual sensation of a sensory stimulus and presented a possible mechanism by which the nervous system can operate. The present work has examined the suitability of the hypothesized mechanism for a large number of physiological properties of the functioning of the nervous system. In addition possible explanations for different clinical conditions were also examined.

XI.1 Memory retrieval at physiological time-scales

Time-scales of gene expression, translation of pre-existing mRNA, post-translational modification of proteins and cascades biochemical reactions are beyond the physiological time-scales of memory retrieval. According to the semblance hypothesis, the activity-induced formation and re-activation of functional LINKs or similar events discussed in section II.6 as potential mechanisms of memory storage and retrieval match with the physiological time-scales.

XI.2 Synaptic plasticity and semblance

Establishment and maintenance functional LINKs during learning requires plasticity changes at the synapses. These changes may require trafficking and reorganization of protein, lipid and carbohydrate molecules. Possible molecular changes during the activation or re-activation of a functional LINK were described as a separate section (section II.8.3). However, since functional LINKs are transient, the extent of structural changes will be for maintenance of the postsynapses to a re-LINKable state (at the time of memory retrieval). The nature of these structural changes needs to be further examined. Once the LINKable state of the functional LINKs is achieved, they can be functionally re-LINKed instantaneously without the requirement of any new protein synthesis at the time of retrieval. This enables memory retrieval at physiological time-scales.

XI.3 Oxygenation-state mediated spread of chemical reaction

By altering the initial oxygenation-state in the modified Golgi staining experiments (section VII.2), spread of chemical reaction was observed most probably between the dendritic spines. It is likely that propagation of the reaction towards the adjacent dendritic spines belonging to different neurons in an oxygenation-state dependent fashion may be responsible for the large number of interconnections (416± 106 (S.D); n = 106) visible at the CA3 region of the hippocampus. This opens possibilities for similar oxygenation-state dependent functional LINKs between the dendritic spines of adjacent neurons at sites of increased signal intensity observed in fMRI. Future experiments are required to study the possibilities for EPSP-spread between simultaneously activated dendritic spines in the presence of an increased local oxygenation-state. Since de-oxygenation state (as evidenced by deoxy-haemoglobin concentrations at BOLD signals in fMRI) peaks nearly 4 to 5 seconds after neuronal activity (98), oxygen may not be directly involved; instead oxygen may replenish the tissue-stores or get used up through oxidative phosphorylation reactions for replenishing high energy molecules. In either condition, an oxygenation-state dependent functional LINK is expected to take place.

XI.4 Need for computational studies and physical systems to test the hypothesis

It will require time to develop advanced techniques to prove the formation and re-activation of the functional LINKs between the postsynaptic membranes using *in vitro* or *in vivo* experiments. As explained before, we can only demonstrate the effect of functional LINKs through interpretations of the changes in neuronal firing or channel currents through whole cell patch clamp experiments (149). Advanced technologies will be required to carry out electrophysiological experiments to prove the presence of the functional LINKs between the two identified postsynaptic membranes.

An artificial system similar to that explained by the semblance hypothesis can possibly be created by using computer programs. Equivalent changes for activity and oxygenation-state dependent functional LINKs can be established between the postsynapses during sessions of associative learning. Once learning is complete, the cue stimulus can be used to re-activate the functional LINKs to induce both the synaptic and network semblances. Since semblances are virtual sensations that are internal properties of a nervous system, we need to incorporate a signal system that gets activated whenever the specific partial network or a subset of postsynapses representing/ belong to the learned item is activated, which will indicate memory retrieval. These efforts may eventually lead to the development of artificial cognitive systems (95).

XI.5 Possible evolutionary changes

In an ecosystem, both the pray and the predator will continue to develop new mechanisms to survive. As the pray learns to respond to the dangers from a cue stimulus, it escapes the predator. As the learning process progresses, it will continue to add newer functional LINKs within its nervous system. As proposed in section II.8.3, if the functional LINKs are used very often, they may get converted to near-structural LINKs. If they are used by many generations, they may get incorporated in the genetic make up of the species towards building structural LINKs as a part of the evolutionary process.

In response to the development of an advanced mechanism in the pray for identifying the cues as threats, the predator also develops mechanisms to overcome the new adaptations made by the pray. It is often found that the predator has more advanced nervous system than the pray. Both the pray and the predator evolves novel mechanisms to overcome each other's adaptation changes. These processes will take place continuously and can be viewed contributing towards evolutionary changes.

Evolving evolutionary advantages provide longevity of the animals. This provides time for more number of hippocampal new neurons to get incorporated into the circuitry and provides more learning and memory storage to take place within a given nervous system. This will eventually demand a larger cortical area where more functional LINKs can be incorporated.

XII. Conclusion

Semblance hypothesis provides a method to explain how associative memory can be stored by synaptic plasticity changes and retrieved at physiological time-scales. The incorporation of synaptic function, synaptic structural plasticity and the ability to explain many of the brain functions make it a possible candidate for memory storage. Even though memory was explained using the present hypothesis, the question is whether the hypothesized basic units can substantiate or lead to understanding of the mechanism of psychiatric diseases and consciousness (Fig.24).

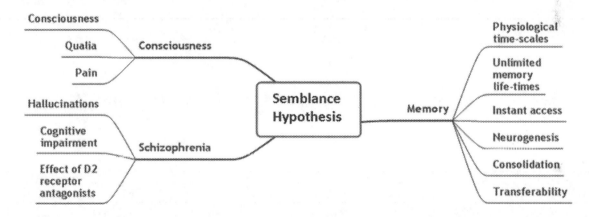

Figure 24.Flowchart showing multiple physiological and pathological conditions that are needed to be explained using the hypothesis. The semblance hypothesis explains the right arm of the flow chart -memory. The success of the hypothesis depends on its ability to explain the left arms of the flow chart, namely consciousness and schizophrenia.

Computational feasibility studies and experiments to study the nature of the functional LINKs during learning are the next major steps. Functional studies to test the hypothesis require proof of spread of activity from one postsynaptic membrane to the neighboring ones through the functional LINKs. Even though experiments carried out by Tye et al (149) provide sufficient corroborative evidence in support of the semblance hypothesis, newer investigations to study possible oxygenation state-dependent changes between the postsynapses may become useful.

Since most of the physiological and pathological conditions of the brain functions as well as the relationship between memory and long term potentiation can be explained based on the synthetic premises that were used to derive the semblance hypothesis for memory, it supports the conclusion that the premises used for deriving the hypothesis are likely true. Searching for further corroborative evidences and conducting further experimental studies to examine the nature of the functional LINKs can provide answers to the validity and sufficiency of the hypothesis.

From the transferability property of the semblances explained in section III.5, it can be seen that memory can be enhanced by large number of unrelated learning. Even though, the number of LINKable postsynapses is finite, combinations/permutations of the semblances from the postsynapses representing the learned items are very large that associative learning events may only be the limiting factor for increasing the memory storage capabilities, provided age-related degenerative changes do not take place. Memory may be reduced by manipulating the molecules that are important in establishing and maintaining the functional LINKs (Fig.20).

The synthetic premise of the existence of the functional LINKs between the postsynapses during learning and their re-activation during memory retrieval is a unique feature of the present hypothesis. Synaptic and network semblances providing virtual sensation of sensory stimuli in a system that receives neural inputs as a continuum, is viewed as memory. The functional LINKs hypothesized by the present hypothesis is able to explain most of the physiological features of memory. Memory formation and its long-term storage through the mechanisms explained by the present hypothesis have the capacity to meet the competing needs for flexibility required to encode memories by modifying the existing brain structure (3, 40, 145). The present hypothesis should be treated as unproved until it is verified against further experimental results.

Acknowledgements

I acknowledge all the support from the Neurosearch Center in Toronto, Canada.

References

1. Abbott LF: Theoretical neuroscience rising. **Neuron** 60:489-495, 2008.
2. Abbott LF, Varela JA, Sen K, Nelson SB: Synaptic depression and cortical gain control. **Science** 275:220-224, 1997.
3. Abraham WC, Robins A: Memory retention--the synaptic stability versus plasticity dilemma. **Trends Neurosci** 28:73-78, 2005.
4. Amaral DG, Dent JA: Development of the mossy fibers of the dentate gyrus: I. A light and electron microscopic study of the mossy fibers and their expansions. **J Comp Neurol** 195:51-86, 1981.
5. Amaral DG, Witter MP: Hippocampal Formation. In The Rat Nervous System, Second Edition, G.Pacinos ed. (San Diego, CA; Academic Press).pp.443-493, 1995.
6. Amit D J, Fusi S: Learning in neural networks with material synapses. **Neural Computation** 6 (5) 957-982, 1994.
7. Ansorge MS, Zhou M, Lira A, Hen R, Gingrich JA: Early-life blockade of the 5-HT transporter alters emotional behavior in adult mice. **Science** 306:879-881, 2004.
8. Bliss TV, Collingridge GL: A synaptic model of memory: long-term potentiation in the hippocampus. **Nature** 361:31-39, 1993.
9. Bontempi B, Laurent-Demir C, Destrade C, Jaffard R: Time-dependent reorganization of brain circuitry underlying long-term memory storage. **Nature** 400:671-675, 1999.
10. Bronson SL, Murphy BL, Walter C, Danzer SC: Structure and complexity of CA3 pyramidal cell thorny excrescences. Society for Neuroscience annual conference. **Poster number 239.25/ E 16**, 2008.
11. Brozoski TJ, Brown RM, Rosvold HE, Goldman PS: Cognitive deficit caused by regional depletion of dopamine in prefrontal cortex of rhesus monkey. **Science** 205:929-932, 1979.
12. Bruel-Jungerman E, Davis S, Laroche S: Brain plasticity mechanisms and memory: a party of four. **Neuroscientist** 13:492-505, 2007.
13. Cajal R: Histologie du Systeme Nerveux de l'Homme et des Vertebres. Vols. I and II, 1909.
14. Chicurel ME, Harris KM: Three-dimensional analysis of the structure and composition of CA3 branched dendritic spines and their synaptic relationships with mossy fiber boutons in the rat hippocampus. **J Comp Neurol** 325:169-182, 1992.
15. Chklovskii DB, Mel BW, Svoboda K: Cortical rewiring and information storage. **Nature** 431:782-788, 2004.
16. Cohen NJ, Ryan J, Hunt C, Romine L, Wszalek T, Nash C: Hippocampal system and declarative (relational) memory: summarizing the data from functional neuroimaging studies. **Hippocampus** 9:83-98, 1999.
17. Courtiere A, Reybaud J, Camilla C, Lobert P, Drouet J, Jadot G: Oxygen-induced modifications of benzodiazepine receptors and D2 dopamine receptors in the rat under hyperoxia. **Free Radic Res Commun** 15:29-34, 1991.

18. Cowan N: Attention and memory: An integrated framework. New York: Oxford University Press., 1995.

19. Cowan N: Attention and Memory, Oxford University Press. 1997.

20. Cowan N: Working memory capacity. New York, NY: Psychology Press. 2005.

21. Crick F, Koch C: A framework for consciousness. **Nat Neurosci** 6:119-126, 2003.

22. Dahlin E, Neely AS, Larsson A, Backman L, Nyberg L: Transfer of learning after updating training mediated by the striatum. **Science** 320:1510-1512, 2008.

23. Dapretto M, Davies MS, Pfeifer JH, Scott AA, Sigman M, Bookheimer SY, Iacoboni M: Understanding emotions in others: mirror neuron dysfunction in children with autism spectrum disorders. **Nat Neurosci** 9:28-30, 2006.

24. Darian-Smith C, Gilbert CD: Axonal sprouting accompanies functional reorganization in adult cat striate cortex. **Nature** 368:737-740, 1994.

25. Davelaar EJ, Goshen-Gottstein Y, Ashkenazi A, Haarmann HJ, Usher M: The demise of short-term memory revisited: empirical and computational investigations of recency effects. **Psychol Rev** 112:3-42, 2005.

26. Doron NN, Ledoux JE: Organization of projections to the lateral amygdala from auditory and visual areas of the thalamus in the rat. **J Comp Neurol** 412:383-409, 1999.

27. Draguhn A, Traub RD, Schmitz D, Jefferys JG: Electrical coupling underlies high-frequency oscillations in the hippocampus in vitro. **Nature** 394:189-192, 1998.

28. Dulay MF, Levin HS, York MK, Mizrahi EM, Verma A, Goldsmith I, Grossman RG, Yoshor D: Predictors of individual visual memory decline after unilateral anterior temporal lobe resection. **Neurology** 72:1837-1842, 2009.

29. Duncan CP: The retroactive effect of electroshock on learning. **J Comp Physiol Psychol** 42:32-44, 1949.

30. Ecker AS, Berens P, Keliris GA, Bethge M, Logothetis NK, Tolias AS: Decorrelated neuronal firing in cortical microcircuits. **Science** 327:584-587, 2010.

31. Erickson MA, Maramara LA, Lisman J: A single brief burst induces GluR1-dependent associative short-term potentiation: a potential mechanism for short-term memory. **J Cogn Neurosci** 22:2530-2540, 2009.

32. Erulkar SD, Weight FF: Extracellular potassium and transmitter release at the giant synapse of squid. **J Physiol** 266:209-218, 1977.

33. Erulkar SD, Weight FF: Ionic environment and the modulation of transmitter release. **Trends Neurosci** 2:298-301, 1979.

34. Fazio F, Perani D, Gilardi MC, Colombo F, Cappa SF, Vallar G, Bettinardi V, Paulesu E, Alberoni M, Bressi S, et al.: Metabolic impairment in human amnesia: a PET study of memory networks. **J Cereb Blood Flow Metab** 12:353-358, 1992.

35. Feldman ML, Peters A: A technique for estimating total spine numbers on Golgi-impregnated dendrites. **J Comp Neurol** 188:527-542, 1979.

36. Franks PW: All or Nothing: Systematicity, transcendental arguments, and skepticism in germal idealism. Cambride, MA: Harvard University Press.p.211, 2005.

37. Frey U, Morris RG: Synaptic tagging and long-term potentiation. **Nature** 385:533-536, 1997.

38. Frotscher M, Seress L, Schwerdtfeger WK, Buhl E: The mossy cells of the fascia dentata: a comparative study of their fine structure and synaptic connections in rodents and primates. **J Comp Neurol** 312:145-163, 1991.

39. Fusi S, Abbott LF: Limits on the memory storage capacity of bounded synapses. **Nat Neurosci** 10:485-493, 2007.

40. Fusi S, Drew PJ, Abbott LF: Cascade models of synaptically stored memories. **Neuron** 45:599-611, 2005.

41. Fuster JM: Memory in the Cerebral Cortex, MIT Press. 1995.

42. Galvan M, Bruggencate GT, Senekowitsch R: The effects of neuronal stimulation and ouabain upon extracellular K+ and Ca2+ levels in rat isolated sympathetic ganglia. **Brain Res** 160:544-548, 1979.

43. Gelbard-Sagiv H, Mukamel R, Harel M, Malach R, Fried I: Internally generated reactivation of single neurons in human hippocampus during free recall. **Science** 322:96-101, 2008.

44. Gogolla N, Caroni P, Luthi A, Herry C: Perineuronal nets protect fear memories from erasure. **Science** 325:1258-1261, 2009.

45. Golgi C: Sulla struttura della sostanza grigia della cervello. **Gass Med Ital Lombardia** 6:244-246, 1873.

46. Gonzales RB, DeLeon Galvan CJ, Rangel YM, Claiborne BJ: Distribution of thorny excrescences on CA3 pyramidal neurons in the rat hippocampus. **J Comp Neurol** 430:357-368, 2001.

47. Hadjikhani N, Joseph RM, Snyder J, Tager-Flusberg H: Anatomical differences in the mirror neuron system and social cognition network in autism. **Cereb Cortex** 16:1276-1282, 2006.

48. Hammer RP, Jr., Lindsay RD, Scheibel AB: Development of the brain stem reticular core: an assessment of dendritic state and configuration in the perinatal rat. **Brain Res** 227:179-190, 1981.

49. Han JH, Kushner SA, Hsiang H-L, Buch T, Waisman A, Bontempi B, Neve RL, Frankland PW, Josselyn SA: Memory disruption by ablating specific neuronal population. Society for neuroscience annual meeting. **Poster number: 194.11/ UU38**, 2008.

50. Harris KM, Perry E, Bourne J, Feinberg M, Ostroff L, Hurlburt J: Uniform serial sectioning for transmission electron microscopy. **J Neurosci** 26:12101-12103, 2006.

51. Hebb DO: *Organization of Behavior* (Wiley, New York). 1949.

52. Henze DA, McMahon DB, Harris KM, Barrionuevo G: Giant miniature EPSCs at the hippocampal mossy fiber to CA3 pyramidal cell synapse are monoquantal. **J Neurophysiol** 87:15-29, 2002.

53. Herholz K: PET studies in dementia. **Ann Nucl Med** 17:79-89, 2003.

54. Herholz K, Carter SF, Jones M: Positron emission tomography imaging in dementia. **Br J Radiol** 80 Spec No 2:S160-167, 2007.

55. Hoogland PV, Wouterlood FG, Welker E, Van der Loos H: Ultrastructure of giant and small thalamic terminals of cortical origin: a study of the projections from the barrel cortex in mice using Phaseolus vulgaris leuco-agglutinin (PHA-L). **Exp Brain Res** 87:159-172, 1991.

56. Hutchinson DS, Summers RJ, Gibbs ME: Energy metabolism and memory processing: role of glucose transport and glycogen in responses to adrenoceptor activation in the chicken. **Brain Res Bull** 76:224-234, 2008.

57. Imayoshi I, Sakamoto M, Ohtsuka T, Takao K, Miyakawa T, Yamaguchi M, Mori K, Ikeda T, Itohara S, Kageyama R: Roles of continuous neurogenesis in the structural and functional

integrity of the adult forebrain. **Nat Neurosci** 11:1153-1161, 2008.

58. Jaholkowski P, Kiryk A, Jedynak P, Ben Abdallah NM, Knapska E, Kowalczyk A, Piechal A, Blecharz-Klin K, Figiel I, Lioudyno V, Widy-Tyszkiewicz E, Wilczynski GM, Lipp HP, Kaczmarek L, Filipkowski RK: New hippocampal neurons are not obligatory for memory formation; cyclin D2 knockout mice with no adult brain neurogenesis show learning. **Learn Mem** 16:439-451, 2009.

59. Jensen O, Tesche CD: Frontal theta activity in humans increases with memory load in a working memory task. **Eur J Neurosci** 15:1395-1399, 2002.

60. Karpicke JD, Roediger HL, 3rd: The critical importance of retrieval for learning. **Science** 319:966-968, 2008.

61. Kepecs A, Uchida N, Zariwala HA, Mainen ZF: Neural correlates, computation and behavioural impact of decision confidence. **Nature** 455:227-231, 2008.

62. Klausberger T, Somogyi P: Neuronal diversity and temporal dynamics: the unity of hippocampal circuit operations. **Science** 321:53-57, 2008.

63. Koch C, Crick F: The zombie within. **Nature** 411:893, 2001.

64. Kocsis JD, Ruiz JA, Cummins KL: Modulation of axonal excitability mediated by surround electric activity: an intra-axonal study. **Exp Brain Res** 47:151-153, 1982.

65. Krivanek JA, McGaugh JL: Facilitating effects of pre- and posttrial amphetamine administration on discrimination learning in mice. **Agents Actions** 1:36-42, 1969.

66. Laatsch RH, Cowan WM: Electron microscopic studies of the dentate gyrus of the rat. I. Normal structure with special reference to synaptic organization. **J Comp Neurol** 128:359-395, 1966.

67. LaBar KS, Cabeza R: Cognitive neuroscience of emotional memory. **Nat Rev Neurosci** 7:54-64, 2006.

68. Laforce R, Jr., Buteau JP, Paquet N, Verret L, Houde M, Bouchard RW: The value of PET in mild cognitive impairment, typical and atypical/unclear dementias: A retrospective memory clinic study. **Am J Alzheimers Dis Other Demen** 25:324-332.

69. Lashley KS: **Mechanisms and Intelligence: A Quantitative Study of Injuries to the Brain (Univ. of Chicago Press, Chicago**, 1929.

70. Lavigne F, Darmon N: Dopaminergic neuromodulation of semantic priming in a cortical network model. **Neurophysiologia**, 2008.

71. LeDoux J: The emotional brain, fear, and the amygdala. **Cell Mol Neurobiol** 23:727-738, 2003.

72. Levine DN, Calvanio R, Rinn WE: The pathogenesis of anosognosia for hemiplegia. **Neurology** 41:1770-1781, 1991.

73. Liaw JS, Berger TW: Dynamic synapse: a new concept of neural representation and computation. **Hippocampus** 6:591-600, 1996.

74. Lisman J: The CaM kinase II hypothesis for the storage of synaptic memory. **Trends Neurosci** 17:406-412, 1994.

75. Lisman JE, Grace AA: The hippocampal-VTA loop: controlling the entry of information into long-term memory. **Neuron** 46:703-713, 2005.

76. Lisman JE, Harris KM: Quantal analysis and synaptic anatomy--integrating two views of hippocampal plasticity. **Trends Neurosci** 16:141-147, 1993.

77. Logothetis NK: What we can do and what we cannot do with fMRI. **Nature** 453:869-878, 2008.

78. Logothetis NK, Pauls J, Augath M, Trinath T, Oeltermann A: Neurophysiological investigation of the basis of the fMRI signal. **Nature** 412:150-157, 2001.

79. Maass W, Zador AM: Dynamic stochastic synapses as computational units. **Neural Comput** 11:903-917, 1999.

80. MacVicar BA, Dudek FE: Electrotonic coupling between granule cells of rat dentate gyrus: physiological and anatomical evidence. **J Neurophysiol** 47:579-592, 1982.

81. Malenka RC, Nicoll RA: Long-term potentiation--a decade of progress? **Science** 285:1870-1874, 1999.

82. Maletic-Savatic M, Malinow R, Svoboda K: Rapid dendritic morphogenesis in CA1 hippocampal dendrites induced by synaptic activity. **Science** 283:1923-1927, 1999.

83. Maren S, Quirk GJ: Neuronal signalling of fear memory. **Nat Rev Neurosci** 5:844-852, 2004.

84. Martin SJ, Grimwood PD, Morris RG: Synaptic plasticity and memory: an evaluation of the hypothesis. **Annu Rev Neurosci** 23:649-711, 2000.

85. Masugi-Tokita M, Tarusawa E, Watanabe M, Molnar E, Fujimoto K, Shigemoto R: Number and density of AMPA receptors in individual synapses in the rat cerebellum as revealed by SDS-digested freeze-fracture replica labeling. **J Neurosci** 27:2135-2144, 2007.

86. Mayford M, Bach ME, Huang YY, Wang L, Hawkins RD, Kandel ER: Control of memory formation through regulated expression of a CaMKII transgene. **Science** 274:1678-1683, 1996.

87. McDonald AJ: Cortical pathways to the mammalian amygdala. **Prog Neurobiol** 55:257-332, 1998.

88. McGaugh JL, Krivanek JA: Strychnine effects on discrimination learning in mice: effects of dose and time of administration. **Physiol Behav** 5:1437-1442, 1970.

89. Medawar P: Is the scientific paper a fraud? **Talk in British Broadcasting Corporation (BBC)**, 1964.

90. Misanin JR, Miller RR, Lewis DJ: Retrograde amnesia produced by electroconvulsive shock after reactivation of a consolidated memory trace. **Science** 160:554-555, 1968.

91. Mistur R, Mosconi L, Santi SD, Guzman M, Li Y, Tsui W, de Leon MJ: Current Challenges for the Early Detection of Alzheimer's Disease: Brain Imaging and CSF Studies. **J Clin Neurol** 5:153-166, 2009.

92. Mongillo G, Barak O, Tsodyks M: Synaptic theory of working memory. **Science** 319:1543-1546, 2008.

93. Morrens M, Wezenberg E, Verkes RJ, Hulstijn W, Ruigt GS, Sabbe BG: Psychomotor and memory effects of haloperidol, olanzapine, and paroxetine in healthy subjects after short-term administration. **J Clin Psychopharmacol** 27:15-21, 2007.

94. Morris RG, Moser EI, Riedel G, Martin SJ, Sandin J, Day M, O'Carroll C: Elements of a neurobiological theory of the hippocampus: the role of activity-dependent synaptic plasticity in memory. **Philos Trans R Soc Lond B Biol Sci** 358:773-786, 2003.

95. Morris RGM, Tarrassenko L, Kenward M: Cognitive systems:Information Processing Meets Brain Science. Elsevier Press, Amsterdam., 2005.

96. Moscovitch M, Nadel L, Winocur G, Gilboa A, Rosenbaum RS: The cognitive neuroscience of remote episodic, semantic and spatial memory. **Curr Opin Neurobiol** 16:179-190, 2006.

97. Murakawa R, Kosaka T: Structural features of mossy cells in the hamster dentate gyrus,

with special reference to somatic thorny excrescences. **J Comp Neurol** 429:113-126, 2001.

98. Murayama Y, Biebetamann F, Meinecke FC, Muller KR, Augath M, Oeltermann A, Logothetis NK: Relationship between neural and hemodynamic signals during spontaneous activity studied with temporal kernel CCA. **Magn Reson Imaging**, 2010.

99. Murtha T, Stasheff SF: Visual dysfunction in retinal and optic nerve disease. **Neurol Clin** 21:445-481, 2003.

100. Nadel L, Moscovitch M: Memory consolidation, retrograde amnesia and the hippocampal complex. **Curr Opin Neurobiol** 7:217-227, 1997.

101. Nakazawa K, Quirk MC, Chitwood RA, Watanabe M, Yeckel MF, Sun LD, Kato A, Carr CA, Johnston D, Wilson MA, Tonegawa S: Requirement for hippocampal CA3 NMDA receptors in associative memory recall. **Science** 297:211-218, 2002.

102. Nicholson C, Bruggencate GT, Steinberg R, Stockle H: Calcium modulation in brain extracellular microenvironment demonstrated with ion-selective micropipette. **Proc Natl Acad Sci U S A** 74:1287-1290, 1977.

103. Nicoll RA: Dorsal root potentials and changes in extracellular potassium in the spinal cord of the frog. **J Physiol** 290:113-127, 1979.

104. Niessing J, Ebisch B, Schmidt KE, Niessing M, Singer W, Galuske RA: Hemodynamic signals correlate tightly with synchronized gamma oscillations. **Science** 309:948-951, 2005.

105. Nishida N, Katamine S, Shigematsu K, Nakatani A, Sakamoto N, Hasegawa S, Nakaoke R, Atarashi R, Kataoka Y, Miyamoto T: Prion protein is necessary for latent learning and long-term memory retention. **Cell Mol Neurobiol** 17:537-545, 1997.

106. Nishitani N, Avikainen S, Hari R: Abnormal imitation-related cortical activation sequences in Asperger's syndrome. **Ann Neurol** 55:558-562, 2004.

107. Nobler MS, Sackeim HA: Neurobiological correlates of the cognitive side effects of electroconvulsive therapy. **J Ect** 24:40-45, 2008.

108. O'Carroll CM, Martin SJ, Sandin J, Frenguelli B, Morris RG: Dopaminergic modulation of the persistence of one-trial hippocampus-dependent memory. **Learn Mem** 13:760-769, 2006.

109. Oertel V, Rotarska-Jagiela A, van de Ven VG, Haenschel C, Maurer K, Linden DE: Visual hallucinations in schizophrenia investigated with functional magnetic resonance imaging. **Psychiatry Res** 156:269-273, 2007.

110. O'Keefe J, Dostrovsky J: The hippocampus as a spatial map. Preliminary evidence from unit activity in the freely-moving rat. **Brain Res** 34:171-175, 1971.

111. Olypher AV, Klement D, Fenton AA: Cognitive disorganization in hippocampus: a physiological model of the disorganization in psychosis. **J Neurosci** 26:158-168, 2006.

112. O'Rourke NA, Fraser SE: Dynamic changes in optic fiber terminal arbors lead to retinotopic map formation: an in vivo confocal microscopic study. **Neuron** 5:159-171, 1990.

113. Osada T, Adachi Y, Kimura HM, Miyashita Y: Towards understanding of the cortical network underlying associative memory. **Philos Trans R Soc Lond B Biol Sci** 363:2187-2199, 2008.

114. Pellerin L, Magistretti PJ: Glutamate uptake into astrocytes stimulates aerobic glycolysis: a mechanism coupling neuronal activity to glucose utilization. **Proc Natl Acad Sci U S A**

91:10625-10629, 1994.

115. Penrose R: Where is there scope for a non-computational physics? in *From Brain to Consciousness*. The Penguin press.167-179, 1998.

116. Poirazi P, Mel BW: Impact of active dendrites and structural plasticity on the memory capacity of neural tissue. **Neuron** 29:779-796, 2001.

117. Popper C: The Logic of Scientific Discovery. 1965.

118. Purves D, Augustine GJ, Fitzpatrick D, Hall WC, LaMantia A-S, McNamara JO, White LE: Neuroscience. 4th ed. Sinauer Associates. P 137-8 ISBN 978-0-87893-697-7., 2008.

119. Ranganath C, Blumenfeld RS: Doubts about double dissociations between short- and long-term memory. **Trends Cogn Sci** 9:374-380, 2005.

120. Rasch B, Buchel C, Gais S, Born J: Odor cues during slow-wave sleep prompt declarative memory consolidation. **Science** 315:1426-1429, 2007.

121. Rizzolatti G, Fogassi L, Gallese V: Neurophysiological mechanisms underlying the understanding and imitation of action. **Nat Rev Neurosci** 2:661-670, 2001.

122. Roskies AL: The binding problem. **Neuron** 24:7-9, 111-125, 1999.

123. Rossato JI, Bevilaqua LR, Izquierdo I, Medina JH, Cammarota M: Dopamine controls persistence of long-term memory storage. **Science** 325:1017-1020, 2009.

124. Routtenberg A: The substrate for long-lasting memory: if not protein synthesis, then what? **Neurobiol Learn Mem** 89:225-233, 2008.

125. Rubin DD, Fusi S: Long memory lifetimes require complex synapses and limited sparseness. **Front Comput Neurosci** 1:7, 2007.

126. Ruchkin DS, Grafman J, Cameron K, Berndt RS: Working memory retention systems: a state of activated long-term memory. **Behav Brain Sci** 26:709-728; discussion 728-777, 2003.

127. Santarelli L, Saxe M, Gross C, Surget A, Battaglia F, Dulawa S, Weisstaub N, Lee J, Duman R, Arancio O, Belzung C, Hen R: Requirement of hippocampal neurogenesis for the behavioral effects of antidepressants. **Science** 301:805-809, 2003.

128. Sawaguchi T, Goldman-Rakic PS: D1 dopamine receptors in prefrontal cortex: involvement in working memory. **Science** 251:947-950, 1991.

129. Schmitz D, Schuchmann S, Fisahn A, Draguhn A, Buhl EH, Petrasch-Parwez E, Dermietzel R, Heinemann U, Traub RD: Axo-axonal coupling. a novel mechanism for ultrafast neuronal communication. **Neuron** 31:831-840, 2001.

130. Scoville WB, Milner B: Loss of recent memory after bilateral hippocampal lesions. **J Neurol Neurosurg Psychiatry** 20:11-21, 1957.

131. Severac Cauquil A, Trotter Y, Taylor MJ: At what stage of neural processing do perspective depth cues make a difference? **Exp Brain Res** 170:457-463, 2006.

132. Shanes AM: Electrochemical aspects of physiological and pharmacological action in excitable cells. II. The action potential and excitation. **Pharmacol Rev** 10:165-273, 1958.

133. Shergill SS, Brammer MJ, Williams SC, Murray RM, McGuire PK: Mapping auditory hallucinations in schizophrenia using functional magnetic resonance imaging. **Arch Gen Psychiatry** 57:1033-1038, 2000.

134. Shors TJ, Miesegaes G, Beylin A, Zhao M, Rydel T, Gould E: Neurogenesis in the adult is involved in the formation of trace memories. **Nature** 410:372-376, 2001.

135. Snow RW, Dudek FE: Evidence for neuronal interactions by electrical field effects in the

CA3 and dentate regions of rat hippocampal slices. **Brain Res** 367:292-295, 1986.

136. Spencer KM, Nestor PG, Niznikiewicz MA, Salisbury DF, Shenton ME, McCarley RW: Abnormal neural synchrony in schizophrenia. **J Neurosci** 23:7407-7411, 2003.

137. Squire LR: Memory and the hippocampus: a synthesis from findings with rats, monkeys, and humans. **Psychol Rev** 99:195-231, 1992.

138. Squire LR: Memory and forgetting: long-term and gradual changes in memory storage. **Int Rev Neurobiol** 37:243-269; discussion 285-248, 1994.

139. Squire LR, Ojemann JG, Miezin FM, Petersen SE, Videen TO, Raichle ME: Activation of the hippocampus in normal humans: a functional anatomical study of memory. **Proc Natl Acad Sci U S A** 89:1837-1841, 1992.

140. Stewart MG, Davies HA, Sandi C, Kraev IV, Rogachevsky VV, Peddie CJ, Rodriguez JJ, Cordero MI, Donohue HS, Gabbott PL, Popov VI: Stress suppresses and learning induces plasticity in CA3 of rat hippocampus: a three-dimensional ultrastructural study of thorny excrescences and their postsynaptic densities. **Neuroscience** 131:43-54, 2005.

141. Tesche CD, Karhu J: Theta oscillations index human hippocampal activation during a working memory task. **Proc Natl Acad Sci U S A** 97:919-924, 2000.

142. Theoret H, Halligan E, Kobayashi M, Fregni F, Tager-Flusberg H, Pascual-Leone A: Impaired motor facilitation during action observation in individuals with autism spectrum disorder. **Curr Biol** 15:R84-85, 2005.

143. Traub RD, Bibbig A, LeBeau FE, Buhl EH, Whittington MA: Cellular mechanisms of neuronal population oscillations in the hippocampus in vitro. **Annu Rev Neurosci** 27:247-278, 2004.

144. Treves A: Graded-response neurons and information encodings in autoassociative memories. **Phys Rev A** 42:2418-2430, 1990.

145. Tse D, Langston RF, Kakeyama M, Bethus I, Spooner PA, Wood ER, Witter MP, Morris RG: Schemas and memory consolidation. **Science** 316:76-82, 2007.

146. Tsien JZ, Huerta PT, Tonegawa S: The essential role of hippocampal CA1 NMDA receptor-dependent synaptic plasticity in spatial memory. **Cell** 87:1327-1338, 1996.

147. Tsodyks M, Feigelman M: Enhanceed storage capacity in neural networks with low level of activity. **Europhys. Lett** 6:101, 1998.

148. Tulving E: Episodic memory: from mind to brain. **Annu Rev Psychol** 53:1-25, 2002.

149. Tye KM, Stuber GD, de Ridder B, Bonci A, Janak PH: Rapid strengthening of thalamo-amygdala synapses mediates cue-reward learning. **Nature** 453:1253-1257, 2008.

150. Vadakkan KI: Semblance of activity at the shared postsynapses and extracellular matrices: A structure-function hypothesis of memory. **iUniverse Publishers, Lincoln, U.S.A.**, 2007.

151. Vadakkan KI: Examination of the premises of semblance hypothesis that explains retrieval-efficient mechanism of memory at appropriate time-scales. **2nd Annual Canadian Neuroscience Meeting abstract number A-G 1188**, 2008.

152. Vadakkan KI: Oxidation-state dependent interconnections between dendritic spines. Society for neuroscience annual meeting 2008. **Abstract number: 239.19/ E16**, 2008.

153. Vadakkan KI: Delusions, cognitive impairment and the therapeutic effect of dopamine receptor antagonists in schizophrenia - An explanation through the semblance hypothesis of memory. Society for Neuroscience annual conference. Abstract number 644.3/U18. 2009.

154. Valiant LG: Memorization and association on a realistic neural model. **Neural Comput** 17:527-555, 2005.

155. van Praag H, Kempermann G, Gage FH: Running increases cell proliferation and neurogenesis in the adult mouse dentate gyrus. **Nat Neurosci** 2:266-270, 1999.

156. Vertes RP, Albo Z, Viana Di Prisco G: Theta-rhythmically firing neurons in the anterior thalamus: implications for mnemonic functions of Papez's circuit. **Neuroscience** 104:619-625, 2001.

157. Vignal JP, Maillard L, McGonigal A, Chauvel P: The dreamy state: hallucinations of autobiographic memory evoked by temporal lobe stimulations and seizures. **Brain** 130:88-99, 2007.

158. Viswanathan A, Freeman RD: Neurometabolic coupling in cerebral cortex reflects synaptic more than spiking activity. **Nat Neurosci** 10:1308-1312, 2007.

159. Volpe BT, Hirst W: The characterization of an amnesic syndrome following hypoxic ischemic injury. **Arch Neurol** 40:436-440, 1983.

160. Wang M, Vijayraghavan S, Goldman-Rakic PS: Selective D2 receptor actions on the functional circuitry of working memory. **Science** 303:853-856, 2004.

161. Warburton EC, Koder T, Cho K, Massey PV, Duguid G, Barker GR, Aggleton JP, Bashir ZI, Brown MW: Cholinergic neurotransmission is essential for perirhinal cortical plasticity and recognition memory. **Neuron** 38:987-996, 2003.

162. Whitlock JR, Heynen AJ, Shuler MG, Bear MF: Learning induces long-term potentiation in the hippocampus. **Science** 313:1093-1097, 2006.

163. Willshaw DJ, Buneman OP, Longuet-Higgins HC: Non-holographic associative memory. **Nature** 222:960-962, 1969.

164. Winson J: Loss of hippocampal theta rhythm results in spatial memory deficit in the rat. **Science** 201:160-163, 1978.

165. Wise RA: Dopamine, learning and motivation. **Nat Rev Neurosci** 5:483-494, 2004.

166. Woolley CS, Gould E, Frankfurt M, McEwen BS: Naturally occurring fluctuation in dendritic spine density on adult hippocampal pyramidal neurons. **J Neurosci** 10:4035-4039, 1990.

167. Yancey SW, Phelps EA: Functional neuroimaging and episodic memory: a perspective. **J Clin Exp Neuropsychol** 23:32-48, 2001.